guaranteed
irish

C000296245

THE ENGLISH WORKBOOK

DEVELOPING LITERACY

Writing forms

Speaking

Grammar

Spelling

Procedure

Listening

Narrative

Reading

Report

Proofreading

Vocabulary

Recount

Exposition

Evaluation

Editing

Diane Henderson   Rosemary Morris   Jenepher Snell

Prim-Ed
Publishing

The English workbook *(Book E)*

Published by Prim-Ed Publishing 2013

Copyright© Diane Henderson, Rosemary Morris, Jenepher Snell 2007

ISBN 978-1-84654-643-3
PR–6280

Titles available in this series:
The English workbook *(Book A)*
The English workbook *(Book B)*
The English workbook *(Book C)*
The English workbook *(Book D)*
The English workbook *(Book E)*
The English workbook *(Book F)*
The English workbook *(Book G)*

Published by
Prim-Ed Publishing

www.prim-ed.com

Introduction

This workbook is all about procedures, recounts, expositions, narratives and reports. These are called writing formats. There are two units of work based on each format.

Completing the exercises in your workbook will help you to understand the five different formats and to learn how to plan and write them yourself.

You will be:

- discussing and working out the structure of each format
- checking that you understand the text by doing some comprehension exercises
- working to improve your vocabulary, spelling, punctuation and grammar
- practising different writing skills
- learning how to check your writing by editing and proofreading
- checking how much you have learned by doing a test at the end of each unit.

Remember: *Good writers need to think about, plan and review their writing; it doesn't just happen.*

Contents

Contents

Contents

The English workbook

Prim-Ed Publishing – www.prim-ed.com

Treating burns and scalds

This procedure explains **how to do something.**
The main purpose is to **direct**, **inform** or **explain**.

Read the **procedure** for treating burns and scalds.

Treating burns and scalds

Aim: To reduce the effect of heat, prevent infection, relieve pain and minimise shock.

Requirements: cold water

clean, sterile, non-fluffy material

Steps:
1. Reassure the patient.
2. Place the injured part under cold, slowly running water.
   OR
   Immerse in cold water for ten minutes. If pain persists, leave longer.
3. Gently remove any rings, watches, belts, shoes or any other clothing from the injured area before it starts to swell.
4. Cover the area with clean, sterile, non-fluffy material.
5. Seek medical advice if burns are severe or extensive.

REMEMBER:
DO NOT use adhesive dressings.
DO NOT apply lotions, ointments or fat to injury.
DO NOT break blisters, remove skin, or interfere with the injured area.
DO NOT remove any material that is sticking to the skin.

If you follow these instructions, pain will be relieved and the wound will heal without infection.

Partner activity

Burns and scalds seriously injure many children every year.

1. (a) Use a dictionary to help you to understand the difference between burns and scalds.

   (b) Discuss possible cause of these types of injury in the home.

   (c) Compile two lists.

   Burns and scalds can be caused by:

Burns	Scalds

2. (a) Select one cause and give your partner instructions for avoiding this type of burn or scald.

   (b) I spoke about preventing injury caused by:

   _____

   (c) The two most important points I made were:

   _____

   _____

   and

   _____

   _____

   (d) My partner spoke about preventing injury caused by:

   _____

   (e) His/Her most important point was:

   _____

   _____

Structure

This procedure has:

A goal: This is at the beginning and tells us what is to be done.

Requirements: These are items needed to complete a task.
For example: ingredients and utensils if cooking
firelighters, matches, wood, paper if setting a fire

Steps: This is a list of instructions written in a particular order.

Test: Was the task completed successfully?

1.   Reread the procedure for treating minor burns. Answer the questions about the structure of the procedure.

Goal	*Requirements*
What is this procedure about?	What do you need to complete this task?

Steps

The order of the steps in a procedure can be very important. Colour the instruction you would do first.

Cover the burn.	OR	Reassure patient.
Immerse burn in water.	OR	Seek medical advice.
Cover with clean bandage.	OR	Remove jewellery.
Speak to a doctor.	OR	Calm the victim.

Test

How would you know if you have followed the procedure correctly?

_____

_____

_____

Reading for information

1. True or false? Colour the correct answer.

    (a) Butter on burns helps to remove the pain. ◯ **true** ◯ **false**

    (b) A clean, sterile bandage will help prevent infection. ◯ **true** ◯ **false**

    (c) The burn is washed with cold water to reduce the pain. ◯ **true** ◯ **false**

    (d) It is important to break blisters if they appear. ◯ **true** ◯ **false**

    (e) The victim must be kept calm. ◯ **true** ◯ **false**

Reading for understanding

1. Why do you think it is important to reassure the injured person?

_____

_____

_____

_____

_____

2. What effect does cold water have on the affected area?

_____

_____

_____

_____

_____

3. Give reasons why it is important to remove jewellery and clothing.

4. Why is it recommended that fluffy material is not used?

_____

_____

_____

_____

5. What would happen to the burn if ointments or fats were applied?

_____

_____

_____

_____

Applying your knowledge

Diagrams can support the steps in procedural text. Reread the procedure
and draw diagrams which show the steps. Label each diagram.

1. Use your dictionary to find the meaning of these words.

    (a) immerse   _____

    _____

    (b) adhesive   _____

    _____

    (c) reassure   _____

    _____

    (d) sterile   _____

    _____

    (e) minimise   _____

    _____

Antonyms

2. Write a word that is opposite in meaning.

    (a) cold   _____

    (b) minimise _____

    (c) under   _____

    (d) sterile _____

    (e) clean   _____

    (f) gentle   _____

    (g) cover   _____

    (h) before   _____

Synonyms

3. Write a word that is similar in meaning.

    (a) severe _____

    (b) advice _____

    (c) persist _____

    (d) prevent _____

Jumbled words

4. Two words from the procedure are jumbled together. Unjumble the words.

    (a) **pndcalio**

    p____ ____ ____

    c____ ____ ____

    (b) **usbrcland**

    b____ ____ ____

    s____ ____ ____ ____

Syllables

Breaking words into smaller parts is a very helpful spelling strategy. Syllables are parts of words with one vowel sound. Words may have one or more syllables.

For example; clean – one syllable, treatment – two syllables.

1. Count the syllables in each word.

    Hint: You may find it helpful to clap the parts of the words and listen for the vowel sounds.

	Word	Syllables			Word	Syllables
(a)	blister			(e)	injury	
(b)	remove			(f)	sterile	
(c)	skin			(g)	infection	
(d)	apply			(h)	medical	

Suffixes

A suffix is a group of letters attached to the end of a word.

For example: **ing   ed   er   ern   ly   est   ful**

There are many spelling rules for adding a suffix, but usually it is just added to the word.

For example: look**ing**   jump**ed**   cold**er**   west**ern**   like**ly**   great**est**   wonder**ful**

Read these rules for adding suffixes.

Rule:

When adding a suffix beginning with a vowel to a word ending with a silent **e**, drop the **e**.

For example: sprink**le**   sprink**ler**   pa**ve**   pa**ving**

requi**re**   requi**ring**   secu**re**   secu**ring**

*The saying '**e** goes away, when **ing** comes to stay', is an easy way to remember part of this rule.*

Rule:

When adding a suffix to words ending with **y**, change the **y** to an **i**.

For example: happ**y**   happ**iness**   sill**y**   sill**ier**

Rule:

When adding the suffixes **er**, **ed**, **est**, **ing**, or **y** to words of **one** syllable, with **one** short vowel, followed by **one** consonant, that consonant is doubled. This is called the one-one-one rule.

For example: run   run**ning**   **run**   **one** syllable

have   **one** short vowel

swim   swim**ming**   **swim**   **one** final consonant

---

2. Add suffixes to these words.

You will need to apply the spelling rules. The first one in each list has been done.

(a) *Just add*

Word	Suffix	Word + suffix
fish	ing	fishing
work	ed	
slow	ly	
east	ern	

(b) *Drop the final e*

Word	Suffix	Word + suffix
brave	est	bravest
hope	ing	
like	ed	
write	er	

(c) *Change the y to an i*

Word	Suffix	Word + suffix
funny	er	funnier
holy	ness	
busy	er	
likely	est	

(d) *One – one – one*

Word	Suffix	Word + suffix
shop	ing	shopping
skip	er	
big	est	
chop	ed	

3. Add suffixes to these words. You will need to apply the different rules you have learnt.

	Word	ing	ed	er	est	ful
(a)	thank					
(b)	sad					
(c)	hope					
(d)	pat					
(e)	manage					
(f)	care					
(g)	thin					
(h)	use					

Verbs

Verbs are the most important words in sentences and describe an action (doing verbs), a state or condition (being verbs) or ownership (having verbs).

1. Underline the verb in each sentence.

   (a) Burns are very painful.

   (b) The young boy tipped hot water over his leg.

   (c) Don't touch the oven.

   (d) Mum drank a cup of hot coffee.

   (e) I burnt my hand.

   (f) John had a burn on his leg.

   (g) The water in the kettle is very hot.

   (h) We have many burns patients in the hospital.

   (i) Dad has a first aid certificate.

   (j) The baby's bottle was too hot.

   (k) His wounds were very painful.

   (l) The doctor treated the child.

2. Write the twelve verbs you underlined in the correct categories in the table below

Remember:

| Being verbs *refer to a state or condition.*
For example:
am   is
are   was
were | Having verbs *refer to ownership.*
For example:
has   have
had | Action verbs *describe an action.*
For example:
looks   washes
cleans   removes |

Being verbs	Having verbs	Action verbs

3. Write sentences using these verbs.

    (a) **Action verbs**

        cover

        wash

    (b) **Being verbs**

        are

        were

    (c) **Having verbs**

        have

        has

    Command verbs

    Statements that start with an action verb and tell someone to do something are called **commands**.

    For example: **Reassure** the patient.   **Apply** a bandage.

    These commands begin with a capital letter and end with a full stop.

4. Reread the procedure *Treatment for minor burns and scalds* and list the command verbs.

    _____

    _____

5. Write a short sentence for each command verb listed below.

    (a) wash

    (b) wipe

    (c) pour

    (d) mix

    (e) boil

Tense

Verbs can change according to **when** an action happens:

Present tense   – **is** happening   For example, He removes

Future tense   – **will** happen   For example, He will remove

Past tense   – **has** happened   For example, He removed

6. These sentences are written in the **present** tense. Rewrite them using the **past** tense; for example: I **am** a singer. I **was** a singer.

   (a) Alex and Andrew are playing tennis.

   _____

   _____

   _____

   (b) Nick wants a party.

   _____

   _____

   _____

   (c) Mr Shay is a popular coach.

   _____

   _____

   _____

   (d) I am going to cricket practice.

   _____

   _____

   _____

   (e) I am waiting for you after school.

   _____

   _____

   _____

7. These sentences are written in the **present** tense. Rewrite them using the **future** tense; for example: She **is working**. She **will work**.

   (a) They are watching TV.

   _____

   _____

   _____

   (b) The cat eats its dinner.

   _____

   _____

   _____

   (c) The grass grows quickly.

   _____

   _____

   _____

   (d) The pool is deserted.

   _____

   _____

   _____

   (e) Sara is lonely.

   _____

   _____

   _____

8. Underline the verb in each sentence and write **present**, **past** or **future** on the line.

    (a) My mother is a fantastic athlete.   _____

    (b) I will train every day.   _____

    (c) My sister is working after school.   _____

    (d) Where is your backpack?   _____

    (e) Dad waited for twenty minutes.   _____

Descriptive verbs

Some verbs are more descriptive than others. Good writers select their verbs carefully to improve their writing and make it more interesting.

9. Choose a more descriptive word from the box to replace the bold words in each sentence. You may need to use a dictionary to check the meaning of some words.

saturated	advanced	obscured
sprinkled	expired	educated
diverted	demolished	penetrated
	originated	

Salt

(a) The traffic was **moved away** from the accident.   _____

(b) Children are **taught** in schools.   _____

(c) An arrow **entered** the target area.   _____

(d) The game of rugby **started** in England.   _____

(e) The time on the parking meter had **run out**.   _____

(f) Mum has always **put** salt on potatoes.   _____

(g) A house in our street was **knocked down**.   _____

(h) The heavy rain **wet** the washing.   _____

(i) The soldiers **went** into enemy territory.   _____

(j) The trees **blocked** our view of the ocean.   _____

Text organisation

A procedure has: *A goal*

A list of requirements

Steps to follow

Test to measure success

Language features

A procedure uses: *Short, clear statements*

Command verbs

Present tense

Study the text organisation and language features of *Treating burns and scalds*.

Text organisation

Language features

Goal – the title summarises the goal

Treating burns and scalds

Equipment and requirements

Aim: To reduce the effect of heat, prevent infection, relieve pain and minimise shock.

Requirements: cold water

clean, sterile, non-fluffy material

Command verbs in the present tense.

Steps:
1. Reassure the patient.
2. Place the injured part under cold, slowly running water.

   OR

   Immerse in cold water for ten minutes. If pain persists, leave longer.
3. Gently remove any rings, watches, belts, shoes or any other clothing from the injured area before it starts to swell.
4. Cover the area with clean, sterile, non-fluffy material.
5. Seek medical advice if burns are severe or extensive.

Steps

Short and clear statements

REMEMBER: **DO NOT** use adhesive dressings.

DO NOT apply lotions, ointments or fat to injury.

DO NOT break blisters, remove skin, or interfere with the injured area.

DO NOT remove any material that is sticking to the skin.

If you follow these instructions, pain will be relieved and the wound will heal without infection.

Test

Treating an injury

After school last Friday, you were walking home with your sister, Mary, who is nine years old. Mary was distracted by a bird in a tree and she tripped on a piece of broken pavement. She fell and grazed her knee.

Write a procedure explaining how you would treat the injury immediately and when you reached home. Remember to use short, clear statements in the correct order.

Aim: _____

_____

Requirements: _____

_____

_____

_____

_____

Steps: _____

_____

_____

_____

_____

_____

_____

_____

_____

_____

_____

Test (How would you know that your treatment was successful?):

_____

_____

Choose **one** topic from the box. Use the framework to plan your procedure, then write it on a separate sheet of paper. You may research the appropriate information on the Internet, in the library or you could ask someone.

> **How to treat:** an ankle sprain
> a snake bite
> an eyelash in the eye
> a nail in the foot

Title:

Aim: _____
_____

Requirements:

Steps: _____
_____
_____
_____
_____
_____
_____
_____
_____
_____
_____
_____
_____

Test: (How do you know if you have been successful?):
_____
_____

Use the checklist below to edit and proofread your work.

You will be self-editing for:

Spelling   Punctuation

Grammar   Sentence structure

You will be using a peer (partner) editor for:

Clear instructions

Sense

Checklist

Title of the procedure: _____

1. Does your procedure make sense to you? .... ◯ **yes** ◯ **no**

2. Did you include a goal? .... ◯ **yes** ◯ **no**

3. Did you list the things you needed? .... ◯ **yes** ◯ **no**

4. Have you included all the steps in the correct order? .... ◯ **yes** ◯ **no**

5. Did you add a test to check that your procedure works? .... ◯ **yes** ◯ **no**

6. Spelling:

    (a)   Have you corrected any spelling errors? .... ◯ **yes** ◯ **no**

    (b)   Did you check that your words looked right? .... ◯ **yes** ◯ **no**

    (c)   Did you use a dictionary? .... ◯ **yes** ◯ **no**

    (d)   Did you ask someone to help you with your spelling? .... ◯ **yes** ◯ **no**

7. Did you use command verbs? .... ◯ **yes** ◯ **no**

8. Are your statements short and clear? .... ◯ **yes** ◯ **no**

9. Did each sentence make sense when you read it on
    its own? .... ◯ **yes** ◯ **no**

10. Do all your statements start with a capital letter and end
    with a full stop? .... ◯ **yes** ◯ **no**

11. Is your procedure written in the present tense? .... ◯ **yes** ◯ **no**

12. Ask a partner to read your procedure.
    Did he or she find it easy to understand? .... ◯ **yes** ◯ **no**

1. Choose a topic from the box and plan and write a procedure. Use a planning sheet then write it on a separate sheet of paper.

Treating nosebleed	*Cooking toast*
Treating a cut toe	*Baiting a fishhook*
Treating sand in the eye	*Playing a DVD*

2. Complete the following statements.

   Text:

   A procedure has a title, a list of

   _____,

   _____, and a

   _____ at the end.

   Language:

   A procedure uses short,

   _____

   statements.

3. Answer the questions.

   (a) In what tense are procedures usually written? _____

   (b) What could happen if the steps were not followed in order?

   _____

   _____

   (c) Why are diagrams sometimes used in procedures?

   _____

   _____

4. (a) Antonyms are words with the _____ meaning.

   (b) Synonyms are words with the _____ meaning.

5. How many syllables in each word?

   (a) doctor ☐   (b) nurse ☐   (c) hospital ☐

   (d) ambulance ☐   (e) treatment ☐   (f) pathology ☐

6. | **ing** | **er** | **est** | **ed** | **ly** | **ness** |
   |---|---|---|---|---|---|

   The above can be added to the end of words and are called _____

7. Add **ing** to these words.

   (a) love _____

   (b) grab _____

   (c) rub _____

   (d) find _____

   (e) talk _____

   (f) brave _____

8. Write a short sentence for each command verb.

   (a) look

   (b) finish

   (c) go

9. Underline the verbs and write **past**, **present** or **future** on the line.

   (a) The girl ran home from school. _____

   (b) Her mother is waiting for her. _____

   (c) Then she will take her to her music lesson. _____

10. Change to the tense written in the brackets and write the sentence below.

   (a) He is walking. (past)

   (b) It will rain. (present)

   (c) I can't find my book. (past)

   (d) The duck swam. (future)

Dog saves friend

ANALYSIS

A recount is a **retelling of past events** in time order.
Recounts can be written in the form of a diary,
a letter, or a newspaper article.

Read the following recount.

Dog saves friend

Bonnie is hugged by her grateful owner,
Wendy Smith and son, Jarrad (18 months)

Jarrad Smith has every reason to thank his mate, Bonnie, a two-year-old labrador, for saving his life on Thursday afternoon.

Jarrad was playing in the backyard of his Surrey Hills home while his mother Wendy worked in the kitchen at the rear of the house, overlooking the garden.

The ball Jarrad was playing with rolled behind the garden shed and Jarrad, followed by his faithful friend Bonnie, went after it. As Jarrad bent down to pick up the ball, Bonnie, snarling savagely, sprang forward, knocking Jarrad off his feet.

Wendy raced outside, startled by Jarrad's screams and the obvious rage of their gentle family pet. She picked up her sobbing child, and then turned her attention to the dog.

Bonnie had moved away from the shed and was in the middle of the lawn, violently battling a one-metre long brown snake. After putting Jarrad safely inside the house and arming herself with a broom, Wendy joined the battle.

Eventually, Bonnie and Wendy succeeded in overcoming the snake and peace was restored. Bonnie was rewarded with a large steak. Jarrad enjoyed an ice-cream and a badly shaken, but very relieved, mother made herself a pot of tea.

Speaking and listening

Class activity

1. Discuss what you know about snakes. You may like to organise your information in this way.

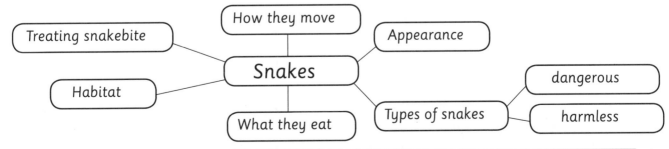

Partner activity

2.   Imagine you are Wendy, Jarrad, Bonnie or the snake. Tell your partner about the incident from your point of view. You will need to make 'I' statements. Remember that your recount must have a **setting** (who, when and why), **events** and an **ending**.

Structure of a recount

Structure

A recount has:

A title: **What** the recount is about

A setting: **Who** was involved, **where** and **when** it happened

The events: **What happened** and the **order** of events

An ending and comment: The **ending** and what the **writer thinks** about it

Read the recount which appeared in the newspaper again and answer the questions.

1.   **Title**   What is the recount about?   _____

2.   **Setting**   (a) Who was the hero?   _____

(b) Who was saved?   _____

(c) Who was there?   _____

(d) Who wrote the recount?   _____

(e) When did it happen?   _____

(f) Where did it happen?   _____

3.   **Events**   (a) Why was Jarrad in the garden?   _____

(b) What was his mother doing?   _____

(c) What happened to the ball?   _____

_____

(d) What did Jarrad do?   _____

(e) Why did Bonnie growl?   _____

(f) What happened to the snake?   _____

4.   **Ending**   (a)   What happened at the end? _____

(b)   How did Jarrad's mother feel when the battle was over?

_____

_____

WORKING WITH THE TEXT   Reading

Reading for information

1.   True or false? Colour the correct answer.

(a)   Jarrad is Wendy's son.   ◯ **true** ◯ **false**

(b)   The ball rolled under the shed.   ◯ **true** ◯ **false**

(c)   Bonnie is a male.   ◯ **true** ◯ **false**

(d)   Bonnie was a bad-tempered, nasty dog.   ◯ **true** ◯ **false**

(e)   Wendy attacked the snake with an axe.   ◯ **true** ◯ **false**

Reading for understanding

1.   (a)   Do you think Bonnie is an intelligent dog?   ◯ **yes** ◯ **no**

Explain why you think this. _____

_____

_____

(b)   Why do you think Wendy put Jarrad inside the house before she went to help Bonnie?

_____

_____

(c)   Why did Wendy give Bonnie a large steak?

_____

_____

(d)   How do you think Wendy felt after this incident?

_____

_____

Applying your knowledge

The order of events in a recount is important. Read the sentences and number them in the correct order from 1–8.

Bonnie grabbed the snake.

Wendy was working in the kitchen.

Jarrad was knocked over.

Wendy gave Jarrad an ice-cream.

The ball rolled behind the shed.

Jarrad screamed.

Jarrad bent down to pick up the ball.

Wendy put Jarrad inside.

Vocabulary

Compound words

Words that are made by joining two smaller words are called **compound words**.

For example: **afternoon** (after + noon)

1. (a) Make the compound words from *Dog saves friend* by joining words from the box.

| ice | back | in | her | side | yard | self | cream |

_____   _____

_____   _____

(b) Find and circle these compound words in the newspaper article *Dog saves friend*.

(c) Write any other compound words you can find in the article.

_____

2. Find and circle the compound word in each sentence.

(a) Sometimes, Jarrad played with his friends in the garden.

(b) He disliked having to stay inside.

(c) Wendy often read the newspaper in the garden.

(d) Dad built a workshop next to the garden.

(e) There was a small waterfall next to the pool.

(f) Jarrad has a yellow raincoat.

Prefixes

A prefix is a word part added to the beginning of a word.

If you know the meaning of the prefix, it can help you to understand the word.

For example: **submarine**

The prefix **sub** means **under**.

So a **sub**marine goes under the water.

1. Write the meanings of these words.

(a) subhuman

(b) subconscious

(c) subsoil

(d) subnormal

(e) substandard

(f) subway

(g) subtitle

2. Write another word using each prefix. Use a dictionary if needed.

(a) **auto** means **self**   automobile   autograph   _____

(b) **multi** means **many**   multipurpose   multimillionaire   _____

(c) **anti** means **against**   antibiotic   antifreeze   _____

Long and short vowel sounds

There are 26 letters of the alphabet:

21 are consonants and 5 are vowels.

The vowels are : _____ _____ _____ _____ _____

Vowels can represent short or long sounds. When we say the vowel letter names in the alphabet, we say **long vowel** sounds.

For example: b**a**by   m**e**   f**i**nd   g**o**   c**u**be

Read these words with **short vowel** sounds, then say the short vowel sounds by themselves.

b**a**nd   s**e**nt   t**i**n   sh**o**p   c**u**t

Vowel sounds may be represented many different ways.

| more than one vowel. |
| For example: b**ea**t (long)   br**ea**d (short) |

| A vowel followed by a consonant. |
| For example: st**ay** (long) |

| Two vowels followed by a consonant. |
| For example: h**air** (long) |

| Two vowels followed by two consonants. |
| For example: w**eigh** (long)   thr**ough** (long) |

| Three vowels. |
| For example: b**eau**tiful (long) |

1. (a) Read these words and circle those with long vowel sounds. Remember to say the words and listen to the sounds.

| have | been | flew | bread | hoped | tooth |
| be | spread | red | paint | running | |

(b) Write a word with a long vowel sound to rhyme with each word.

Try to think of words with the same vowel sound but represented by different letters; for example, **fight**, **bite**.

bl**ew**

f**ee**d

s**ai**l

s**oa**p

sk**y**

thr**ough**

sh**a**d**e**

g**o**

Representing vowel sounds

Look at these different ways to represent the same vowel sound.

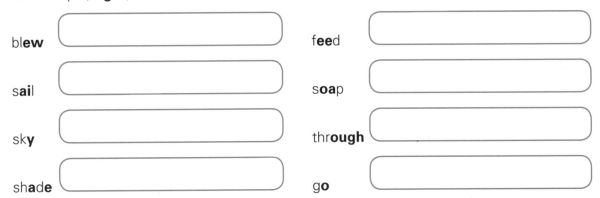

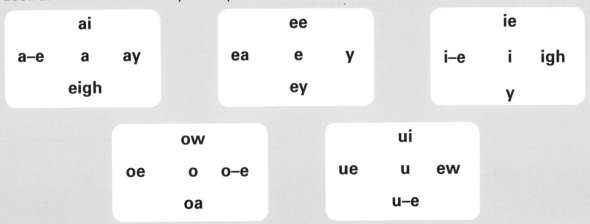

Good spellers need to know about the different ways to represent sounds and to be able to choose the correct one.

2. Choose the correct form to complete these sentences. The first one has be done.

(a) Horses like to eat h_ay_____. (**a**, **ai**, **ay**)

(b) Birds can fl____ h_____. (**ie**, **y**, **igh**)

(c) I like to r____d____ my b____k____. (**y**, **i–e**, **igh**)

(d) Sh____ me your sore t_____. (**o**, **ow**, **oe**)

(e) The l_____f fell form the tr_____. (**ee**, **y**, **ea**)

(f) He r____d____ his horse on the r_____d. (**o**, **o–e**, **oa**)

(g) It is tr_____ that you gr_____ those tomatoes? (**u–e**, **ue**, **ew**)

(h) We c____m____ home from the football g____m____ on the tr_____n. (**ai**, **ay a–e**)

Nouns

Nouns are names for people, places and things.

For example: **doctor**   **hospital**   **needle**

Read this passage. The bold words are *nouns*.

> The faithful **dog** saved **Jarrad** by attacking the **snake** in their **garden**.
>
> **Jarrad** and his **mother** thought that their **dog**, **Bonnie**, was a **hero**.

Some of the nouns have capital letters. These are called *proper nouns*.

For example: **Jarrad**   **Bonnie**

Proper nouns

Proper nouns have capital letters because they are the special names of days, months, people, and places.

1. Complete these sentences using **proper nouns**.

    (a) My name is _____ and I live in _____ .

    (b) I was born in the month of _____ in _____ .

    (c) Today is _____ .

    (d) The name of my school is _____ .

Recognising nouns

If you can put the words **the**, **a** or **some** in front of a word, it is a noun.

For example: The dog can **bark** loudly

  I saw **bark** on the ground near the tree.

You couldn't say: The dog can (a/the/some) **bark** loudly.

But you could say: I saw (the/some) **bark** on the ground.

So **bark** is a noun in the second sentence, but not in the first.

2. Is the bold word a noun? Tick yes or no.

    (a) I would like to have a **bit** of that apple.   ◯ **yes** ◯ **no**

    (b) The dog **bit** the snake.   ◯ **yes** ◯ **no**

    (c) Please **wash** the car.   ◯ **yes** ◯ **no**

    (d) The campers had a **wash** in the river.   ◯ **yes** ◯ **no**

    (e) Mum had a **look** for the snake.   ◯ **yes** ◯ **no**

    (f) **Look** at that beautiful bike.   ◯ **yes** ◯ **no**

3. Write a sentence using each of these words as a noun.
Remember: A word is a noun if you can say **a**, **the** or **some** in front of it.

walk	fight	water	book	paddle

(a) _____

_____

(b) _____

_____

(c) _____

_____

(d) _____

_____

(e) _____

_____

Conjunctions

Conjunctions are joining words. They are used to join sentences.

For example: Jarrad was playing in the garden.

His mother, Wendy, watched him through the window.

New Sentence:
While Jarrad was playing in the garden, his Mother, Wendy, watched him through the window.

4. Underline the conjunction in each sentence. You may like to find the two smaller sentences first.

(a) If you are working late tonight, take a warm jumper to wear home.

(b) I would like to visit Paris before I am too old.

(c) Mandy lost her new necklace because she didn't do it up properly.

(d) Brad was disappointed when he wasn't selected for the team.

(e) The horse tossed its rider off when it was frightened by the snake.

(f) Although it was hot, Sandy was wearing her coat.

5. Make one sentence by joining the two given sentences using any of the conjunctions below.
    (You may like to compare sentences with a partner when you have finished.)

    because   when   although   if   after   so   while

    (a) It is hot.
        I like ice-cream.

    (b) The teacher was cross.
        The class made a lot of noise.

    (c) The team trains very hard.
        The coach is excellent.

    Conjunctions can be placed either at the beginning or in the middle of the sentence.
    For example
    If I work hard, I will get better marks.   Or   I will get better marks **if** I work hard.

6. Find and underline the conjunction then rewrite the sentences starting with the conjunction.
    (Don't forget the capital letter.)

    (a) I clean my teeth before I go to bed.

    _____

    _____

    (b) My puppy chewed my socks while I was asleep.

    _____

    _____

    (c) I had to mow the lawn because Dad had a sore back.

    _____

    _____

    (d) I am a fast runner, although I am a bit overweight.

    _____

    _____

    (e) I stay up late when my favourite show is on TV.

    _____

    _____

Headlines

Newspapers usually have a headline or title for articles throughout the paper. This is especially important on the front page. The reason for adding these headlines is to attract attention so that the reader will want to read the recount and find out what happened.

1. Read these headlines and decide which you would be interested in reading.
Number them in order of interest.

- **Bag snatcher caught by grandmother**
- **Parents punished**
- **Sportsstar in disgrace**
- **Slimming drug fatal**
- **Shark attacks again**
- **Homework to be banned**

2. Headlines or headers need to be:

- **Brief**
- **Interesting**
- **Relevant**
- **Tantalising**
- **Informative**
- **Exciting**

How well does the headline you selected as number 1 rate on each of these items? Write 1–4 in each box, with 4 being the best .

3. Think of a headline for these popular, well-known fairy tales.

For example: *Little Red Riding Hood*   'Wolf eats grandmother'

The three pigs

Cinderella

The three billygoats gruff

Goldilocks and the three bears

Read the newspaper article *Dog saves friend* again. Write a letter from
Wendy to her mother (Jarrad's grandmother), telling her about this event.
Use the plan below then write your letter on a separate sheet of paper.

Title	

Setting	who
	where
	when
	why

Events   1. _____

_____

_____

2. _____

_____

_____

3. _____

_____

_____

4. _____

_____

_____

Concluding statement/comment

After you have written your recount, use the checklist below.

Tick the boxes as you edit and proofread your work.

Checklist

Does your writing include the following?

Title: _____

1. **Setting**:

   (a) who?... ○ **yes** ○ **no**

   (b) what?.. ○ **yes** ○ **no**

   (c) where? .... ○ **yes** ○ **no**

   (d) when? .... ○ **yes** ○ **no**

2. **Events**:

   Written in the correct order? .... ○ **yes** ○ **no**

3. **Statement**:

   A concluding comment which links the story? .... ○ **yes** ○ **no**

4. **Spelling**:

   (a) Have you corrected mistakes? .... ○ **yes** ○ **no**

   (b) Have you used a dictionary or thesaurus?................ ○ **yes** ○ **no**

5. **Grammar**:

   (a) Have you used capital letters correctly?................... ○ **yes** ○ **no**

   (b) Have you used correct punctuation?
        (full stops, commas, apostrophes) .... ○ **yes** ○ **no**

   Have you asked a partner to read your recount? .... ○ **yes** ○ **no**

   Did it make sense?.. ○ **yes** ○ **no**

   Did your partner correct any errors?.................................. ○ **yes** ○ **no**

1. Choose a topic from the box and plan, then write, a recount suitable for a newspaper on a separate sheet of paper.

> *Elephant gatecrashes party*   *School bus terror*
>
> *Dramatic pool rescue*   *Mouse delays flight*

2. Complete the following statements:

   (a) **Text:**

   A recount is _____

   _____

   _____

   _____

   _____

   (b) **Structure:**

   A recount has:

   A title _____

   _____

   _____

   _____

3. Complete the sentences.

   (a) The setting provides information about _____, _____,

   _____ and tells why the events happen.

   (b) The events are told in the _____ in which they happen.

   (c) The concluding statement tells the reader what the writer _____ about the events.

4. Complete the following.

   (a) Words that are made by joining two smaller words are called

   _____ words.

   (b) Join two of these words to make longer words.

no	run	in	them
with	foot	way	path
out	body	side	selves

   _____

   _____

   _____

   _____

5. (a) A prefix is a word part added to the

   _____ of a word.

   (b) Circle the prefix in each word.

   return   **subway**

   antifreeze   **postwar**   **multigrips**

   (c) Which prefix means 'under'?

   _____

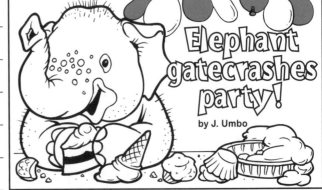

Elephant gatecrashes party!
by J. Umbo

6. (a) Underline the seven nouns in these sentences.

> My birthday is in January.
>
> The teacher was too busy to help his class clean up the playground.
>
> They enjoyed their visit to Waterworld.

(b) Which two are proper nouns? _____, _____.

7. Underline the conjunction in each sentence.

(a) Please clean your teeth before you go to bed.

(b) She burnt her leg because she stood too close to the heater.

(c) Brendan was not allowed to watch TV during the week, but he could watch it on the weekend.

(d) Although it was hot, he wore a warm jumper.

8. Choose the correct long vowel sound to complete the words in these sentences.

(a) M_____k_____'s new k_____t_____ soared h_____ up into the sky. (**igh**, **i–e**, **y**)

(b) Don't thr_____ your ball onto the r_____d. (**ow**, **oa**, **o-e**)

(c) Pl_____se may I r_____d my book b_____fore I go to sl_____p? (**ee**, **ea**, **e**)

(d) Th_____ must w_____t here until the teachers s_____ that it is time

to pl_____. (**ay**, **ai**, **ey**)

(e) You can _____s_____ my n_____ bl_____ pen and a f_____ of my coloured pencils. (**u-e**, **ue**, **ew**)

9. Is the bold word a noun?

(a) There are many lambs born in the **spring**. ◯ **yes** ◯ **no**

(b) He will **spring** into action soon. ◯ **yes** ◯ **no**

(c) I can't **part** with the last two kittens of the litter, so I'll have to keep them. ◯ **yes** ◯ **no**

(d) One **part** of this puzzle is missing. ◯ **yes** ◯ **no**

Sports prefect

Expositions are written or spoken to **persuade others** to **think** or **do something**.

Read this speech about the election of school prefects.

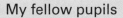

My fellow pupils

Allow me to introduce myself. My name is Ellie McDonald and I am standing for election as the school Sports Prefect for next year. Please take a minute to listen to why I believe I am your best choice for this important position.

I have been a pupil of Moorecroft School since 1st Class. I know the school, I know the area and I grew up with most of the pupils. Moorecroft is *my* school, and I have a strong sense of loyalty towards it.

My sports interests are very wide, both at school and at home. At school, I have been Captain of the swimming team, and have played netball and tennis in the school teams. Outside school, I am on the County Junior Archery Team, and hope to be able to compete in the next Commonwealth Games trials.

Those of you who know me well know that I am fair, easy to approach and talk to and dedicated to sport and our school. These are all qualities that I believe a Sports Prefect *must* have.

If I am elected, I promise to work my hardest for sport, for Moorecroft, and for YOU. My very first task will be to approach the Parents' Association on your behalf and ask them for increased funding to replace the old and worn-out equipment used by the school's cricket teams. I also hope to start a long-term fundraising plan to buy a school bus, so that interschool teams can go to their matches in comfort.

A vote for me will be a vote for the benefit of ALL Moorecroft pupils.

On Voting Day, vote ⬚1⬚ for me, Ellie McDonald, for Sports Prefect.

Speaking and listening

Partner activity

1. (a) Would you vote for Ellie McDonald?　　◯ **yes** ◯ **no**

   (b) Tell your partner the reasons for your decision.

   (c) Working with your partner, compile a list of the five most important qualities you think a sports prefect needs.

Class activity

2. Discuss these issues.

    (a) How important is sport at school?

    (b) Is there too much or too little time spent on sport at your school?

3. (a) Brainstorm positive and negative aspects of sport.

    (b) Prepare a two-minute talk on either:

    > **Sport – a waste of time**   **Sport – the most important subject at school**

    Remember, your task is to persuade others to agree with your views.

Structure of an exposition

An exposition can promote by using persuasive language.

Structure

A title: Tells what the exposition is about.

An overview: Briefly tells what the speaker thinks about the subject.

Reasons: Arguments to persuade people.

Conclusion: Final comment and summing up.

Read the election speech again. Answer the questions.

1. **Title**   What is the speech about? _____

2. **Overview**   What does the speaker want people to do? _____

    _____

3. **Reasons**   (a) How long has Ellie been at the school? _____

    (b) Why does she have a strong sense of loyalty to the school?

    _____

    _____

    (c) What sports has Ellie played for the school? _____

    _____

    (d) What sport does she hope to compete in at an international level? _____

    (e) What does Ellie want the school to help buy? _____

4. **Conclusion** What does Ellie want the pupils to do on voting day?

    _____

Reading for information

1. True or false? Colour the correct answers.

   (a) Ellie played in the school netball and hockey teams.   ◯ **true** ◯ **false**

   (b) Ellie is a good swimmer.   ◯ **true** ◯ **false**

   (c) Moorecroft School has both primary and secondary pupils.   ◯ **true** ◯ **false**

   (d) Ellie is going to the trials for the Commonwealth Games
       swimming team.   ◯ **true** ◯ **false**

   (e) Ellie wants the school to raise money to buy a new school bus.   ◯ **true** ◯ **false**

Reading for understanding

1. How could Ellie know that the school needed new cricket equipment?

   _____

   _____

   _____

   _____

   _____

   _____

2. Do you think that the school already has a school bus?   ◯ **yes** ◯ **no**

   What makes you think this?

   _____

   _____

   _____

   _____

   _____

3. Do you think Ellie cares about her school?   ◯ **yes** ◯ **no**

   Explain why you think this.

4. Do you think Ellie would make a good sports prefect?   ◯ **yes** ◯ **no**

   Explain your reasons.

Applying your knowledge

A sports prefect has a leadership role in a school. Not all pupils are interested in becoming leaders or have the necessary qualities to make a good leader.
Ellie believes she would make a really good leader.

1. (a) What are some of the qualities she says that she has? Make a list.

Quality	Important?
	⚪ **yes** ⚪ **no**
	⚪ **yes** ⚪ **no**
	⚪ **yes** ⚪ **no**
	⚪ **yes** ⚪ **no**
	⚪ **yes** ⚪ **no**
	⚪ **yes** ⚪ **no**

(b) Do you agree that these qualities are important? Tick **yes** or **no** for each one above.

(c) List some other qualities that you think a sports prefect needs.

2. (a) Write the name of a leader you know. _____

(b) Write the name of a boss you know. _____

(c) What is one difference between a leader and a boss?

_____

_____

_____

_____

Compound words

Compound words are made up of two or more smaller words.

1.   Join pairs of these words to make compound words used in the exposition *Sports prefect*.

side	**fund**	**to**	**ball**
school	**wards**	**out**	**inter**
wealth	**Common**	**raising**	**net**

_____   _____

_____   _____

_____   _____

Alphabetical order

2.   Write these words in correct alphabetical order.

(a) **talk   team   tennis   trials   task   their   there**

(b) **start   standing   school   pupil   strong   sense   sport**

_____   _____

_____   _____

_____   _____

_____   _____

3.   (a) Cross out the letters b, p and s to read the message.

┌─────────────────────────────┐
│   │
└─────────────────────────────┘

(b) Cross out the letters n, u and d.

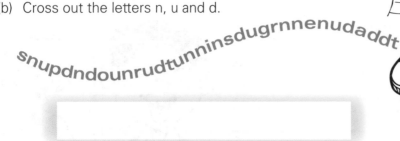

┌─────────────────────────────┐
│   │
└─────────────────────────────┘

Word sleuth

4. (a) Find and colour these words. They are horizontal, vertical or diagonal.

hope	prefect
pupil	sport
loyalty	vote
captain	new
netball	used
elected	old
promise	bike
school	toss
comfort	boot
team	time
know	your
best	me

w	p	p	c	a	p	t	a	i	n
l	e	u	e	s	p	o	r	t	e
a	s	p	b	h	p	o	l	d	t
l	p	i	s	o	r	v	c	e	b
o	r	l	c	p	o	o	v	i	a
y	e	n	h	e	m	t	k	o	l
a	f	t	o	f	i	e	k	t	l
l	e	e	o	f	s	o	n	t	r
t	c	r	l	b	e	u	o	e	n
y	t	i	m	e	e	s	w	a	e
y	o	u	r	s	s	e	l	m	w
e	l	e	c	t	e	d	l	i	e

(b) The leftover letters are _____

(c) Use the leftover letters to make a sentence about Ellie.

┌──┐
│   │
└──┘

5. Construct your own word sleuth for a partner to complete. Choose 10 to 15 words from the exposition.

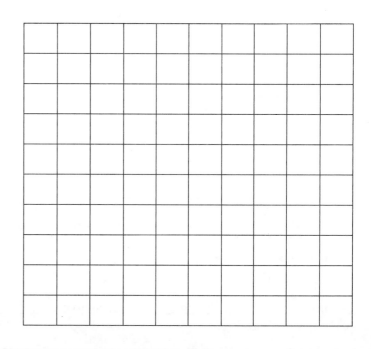

Words

Homophones

Words that look different but sound the same are called *homophones*.

> Read these three words. They are homophones.
>
>   **there**   **their**   **they're**

These three words are often spelled incorrectly because people don't understand what they mean.

there

- Can be used to describe a place.

  For example:

  It is over **there**.

- Can be used with the verb 'to be'.

  For example:

  There is a boy.

  There are some trees.

  There was a storm.

  There were many children.

their

- Is used to show that something belongs to someone.

  For example:

  Their car is blue.

  Their dog ran away.

they're

- Is used instead of the words 'they' and 'are'. The apostrophe is used because the 'a' of 'are' is missing.

  For example:

  They're very busy.

  They're my friends.

1. Choose the correct words to complete the sentences. Remember, some need capital letters!

   > **there**   **their**   **they're**

   (a) _____ team won the cricket match.

   (b) They drove _____ in the school bus.

   (c) _____ trying very hard to win the game.

   (d) Put your sports bags over _____ .

   (e) _____ was a loud cheer when he kicked a goal.

   (f) They looked everywhere but they couldn't find _____ coach.

   (g) They were very pleased with the way _____ players behaved after they lost the game.

   (h) _____ playing _____ next game at school.

Spelling tip

>   **there**   **their**   **they're**
>
> These three words all start with the same three letters (the) and all have the letter 'r'.
> Complete the three words.
>
> the_____ _____   the _____ _____   the_____'_____ _____

Contractions

In English we often leave out letters when two words are joined. An apostrophe is used to indicate that letters have been omitted; for example, **they are** ⟶ **they're**. There are some exceptions; e.g. **won't** and **shan't**.

2. Change the bold words to contractions and write them on the lines below.

    (a) **I would** like to be a prefect.

    _____

    (b) **She will** make an excellent leader.

    _____

    (c) Please **do not** forget to vote.

    _____

    (d) He **will not** vote for her.

    _____

    (e) They **can not** all be prefects.

    _____

    (f) We **did not** win the game.

    _____

    (g) They **were not** at school today.

    _____

    (h) **We had** been very busy.

    _____

    (i) These shoes **are not** comfortable.

    _____

3. Use any suitable contraction to complete the sentence. (Remember to use capital letters in some sentences.)

    (a) _____ forget my

    sports bag.

    (b) The teacher thought

    _____ do well in

    the test.

    (c) _____ playing

    well this week.

    (d) I think _____ be

    great team members.

    (e) _____ be all

    right.

    (f) My mother thought _____

    be late.

    (g) He believes _____ be a

    great puppet.

    (h) If _____ not careful it

    will break.

Punctuation

1. (a) Read these passages.

    (i) one very dark stormy night we decided to go out and buy some hamburgers we were feeling so hungry on the way there it started to rain we all got very wet by the time we arrived home the hamburgers were cold and wet we didn't enjoy them much

    (ii) I really love hamburgers. They must be my favourite food. My mother says that they are not very healthy and she only lets me have one on the weekend. It's not fair. My friend, Ben, can have lots of them.

    (b) Which passage was easier to read and understand?   (i) or (ii)

    (c) Which was quicker to read?   (i) or (ii)

    (d) Why do you think one passage was easier? _____

    _____

    One difference between (i) and (ii) is the punctuation. Punctuation usually helps readers to read and to understand. Did it help you?

    (e) Go back to passage (i) and add the full stops and capital letters. It isn't always easy to work out sentences. Ask someone to read passage (i) with your punctuation and ask if he or she agrees with the sentences you have made.

    Question marks

    How old are you?   Do you like ice-cream?
    Can you ride a bike?   What is your favourite book?
    Where do you live?

    Notice that all of the questions above have question marks at the end.

2. (a) Write three questions you could ask someone who plays sport professionally.

    • _____

    _____

    • _____

    _____

    • _____

    _____

    (b) Check that you started with a capital letter and ended with a question mark.

Commas

Commas are used in writing to:

• separate words in lists,

• show where to have a short pause.

For example: Jill, Peter, Tom and Sue were going to school on the bus, but it was early
and they all missed it.

Look at the commas and work out why they were used.

3. Add commas where they are needed.

(a) The slow old grey dog barked at the children but didn't chase them.

(b) Please go to the shop and buy me some bread eggs sugar and milk then bring them
straight home.

(c) My friends yelled shouted jumped and waved their arms when our school won its first
football grand final last Saturday.

(d) On Sunday night I am allowed to sit in the family room eat my dinner and watch TV then I
have a shower clean my teeth put on my pyjamas and go to bed.

Apostrophes for ownership

Apostrophes can be used to indicate ownership.

For example: the school's prefects   The prefects belong to the school.

the captain's jumper   The jumper belongs to the captain.

Notice that the apostrophe is placed directly after the owner.

If there is more than one owner, the apostrophe is still placed after the owners,
but it looks quite different.

For example: the ants' nest   The nest belonging to the ants.

the prefects' blazers   The blazers belonging the prefects.

4. Circle the owner or owners in each of these.
Remember, the apostrophe is placed after the owner or owners.

(a) the babies' toys   (b) their sons' room

(c) the sheep's back   (d) the frog's legs

(e) the horses' hooves   (f) the table's shape

> Apostrophes can indicate different meanings.
>
> the son's hats **means** one son
>
> the sons' hats **means** more than one son

5. Write singular (s) (one owner) or plural (p) (more than one owner) after each of these:

    (a) the girls' party ☐   (b) the table's legs ☐   (c) the pool's filters ☐

    (d) the teacher's cars ☐   (e) the chefs' hats ☐   (f) the criminal's records ☐

6. Write these using an apostrophe to show ownership.

    (a) the bikes belonging to the boys

    _____

    (b) the computers belonging to the school

    _____

    (c) the flags belonging to the teams

    _____

    (d) the tyres belonging to the tractors

    _____

    (e) the clothing belonging to the women

    _____

WRITING **Activities**

Titles

Titles are important. Titles explain or give clues as to what a piece of writing is about. A good title is the first chance an author has to capture a reader's attention.

A good title: • attracts attention
               • relates to the topic
               • explains the topic using up to six words
               • is easy to remember

1. Read these passages and write a title for each.

(a) Title

Off the east coast of the United States, in the Gulf of Maine, there is a humpback whale that I have known for over fifteen years. Her name, at least the name I have given her, is Sandy. She has a white stripe across her dorsal fin, which looks like beach sand that has been glued to her. Sandy is a large female and the mother of at least four offspring.

(b) Title

Hunting is a major activity for whales. Some, like the baleen whales, feed for only parts of the year. Others eat year round and do not undergo seasonal fasts. Baleen whales feed on small schooling fish or tiny organisms. Sperm whales take larger fish and squid and killer whales eat other marine animals.

Fact and opinion

Expositions try to persuade people to think or do something by presenting **opinions** as **facts**.

For example:

'I am fair, easy to approach and talk to and dedicated to sport and our school.'

2. Read *Sports prefect* again and find four **facts** to add to this list.

(a) I was captain of the swimming team.

(b) _____

(c) _____

(d) _____

(e) _____

3. Find four **opinions** to add to this list.

(a) I am your best choice.

(b) _____

(c) _____

(d) _____

(e) _____

Choose a title from the box below and write an exposition. It may be in the form of an essay, a letter or a speech. Use the plan to help you organise your ideas. Then write your exposition in full on a separate sheet of paper.

Compulsory school sport   *Good sporting conduct*

School uniforms   *Computers in schools*

Title

_____

Introductory statement

(What do you believe?)

_____

_____

Arguments

(Thoughts and ideas which support what you believe.)

_____

_____

_____

_____

_____

_____

_____

_____

_____

_____

_____

_____

Conclusion

(Link your ideas together to form a final comment which summarises your position.)

_____

_____

_____

_____

After you have written your exposition, use the following checklist to edit and proofread your work.

You will need to self-edit for:

Spelling   Punctuation

Grammar   Sentence structure

You will be using a peer (partner) editor for:

Arguments sequenced from strongest to weakest

Sense

Checklist

Title of exposition: _____

1. Do you understand the purpose of an exposition?................................ ◯ **yes** ◯ **no**

2. Does your exposition:

    (a)   clearly state a problem in the introduction? .... ◯ **yes** ◯ **no**

    (b)   provide background information? .... ◯ **yes** ◯ **no**

    (c)   list reasons to support your belief or view? .... ◯ **yes** ◯ **no**

    (d)   use facts to support arguments? .... ◯ **yes** ◯ **no**
          (diagrams, photographs, facts and figures)

    (e)   sequence arguments from strongest to weakest? .... ◯ **yes** ◯ **no**

    (f)   include a final paragraph which reinforces and
          summarises main points?.. ◯ **yes** ◯ **no**

3. Have you used persuasive words? .... ◯ **yes** ◯ **no**

4. Ask your partner to read your exposition.

    (a)   Did she/he understand your point of view?.................................... ◯ **yes** ◯ **no**

    (b)   Did it make sense?... ◯ **yes** ◯ **no**

    (c)   Were you able to persuade your partner to agree with your
          point of view? .... ◯ **yes** ◯ **no**

1. Choose a topic from the box and write an exposition in full on a separate sheet of paper. The exposition may be in the form of an essay, a speech or a letter. Use a framework.

> *Competitive sport for young children*
> *School captains*
> *Punishing bullies*

2. Complete the following.

Expositions are written to _____ others to think or do something.

An exposition can be in the form of a _____.

Structure of an exposition An exposition has:

-   _____a title_____
-   _____
-   _____
-   _____

3. Complete these statements about expositions.

(a) The title tells _____

(b) The overview tells what the writer _____

_____

(c) The _____ are the arguments which try to persuade the audience.

(d) The conclusion is the _____

_____

4. Join pairs of these words to make compound words.

rain	snow	play	coat	foot	place
ball	fire	arm	ground	chair	man

_____ _____ _____

_____ _____ _____

5. Write these words in alphabetical order.

(a) breakfast   brakes   before   bargain   banana

_____

_____

(b) follow   flower   fast   fish   famous   feet

_____

_____

6. Use the correct word to complete each sentence.
   Remember some words need capitals.

there	their	they're

   (a) _____ my shoes.

   (b) They lost _____ way.

   (c) _____ dog had six puppies.

   (d) Go and sit over _____ .

   (e) _____ are five people in our family.

   (f) I think that _____ going to be in trouble for leaving the tap on.

7. Write the sentences using contractions to replace the words in bold print.

   (a) My sister **will not** attend training if **it is** raining but **I will** be there.

   _____

   _____

   (b) **They will** be playing tennis with us tomorrow, but **I am** worried because **we are** not fit and **they are** super-fit and play really well.

   _____

   _____

8. Punctuate these sentences using full stops, question marks and capital letters.

   (a) the boys enjoyed surfing

   (b) do you like going to the beach

   (c) why do you need to wear a hat

9. Add commas where they are needed.

   (a) My uncle used to work hard but now he enjoys reading cooking swimming and golf.

   (b) Don't forget to take your hat sunscreen towel shoes and sunglasses to the beach.

Home alone

A narrative describes a **series of events** and **circumstances** often involving fictitious characters.

Read this narrative.

After spending a few days swimming, windsurfing and fishing at their beach cottage, Jessica, her mum, dad and sister, Melissa, were stuck in the hot, cramped, overloaded car on their way home.

Jessica hated the long drive. It took about an hour and a half and it was so boring. There was nothing to see or do. Melissa was fine—she had her Christmas present, a new MP3 player.

As usual, Dad was playing his favourite driving music, 'Bat out of hell' by Meatloaf. Jessica had no choice but to listen, too. It was driving her bats!

Mum, who was suffering the loud music in silence, suddenly remarked 'We do have the cat … don't we?' Dad took no notice and continued singing along to his music. Melissa, who couldn't hear anything but her own music, did nothing. Jessica panicked.

'Stop, Dad, stop! We must have left Cheong behind', she yelled. Dad stopped singing, but continued driving with a face like thunder. While Jess became hysterical, Mum and Dad calmly outlined their options. They had planned to go back the following weekend; could the cat survive alone for three days? Was there anyone they could ask to feed him? Was he inside or outside the house? Would it be possible to find him?

Melissa, who had noticed the look of terror on her sister's face, actually unplugged her music. 'What's up, Popette?' she queried. 'We've left Cheong behind', cried Jess. Tears were now rolling down her cheeks.

'Last time I saw him he was asleep on the top bunk', Melissa stated calmly. 'We'll just have to go back and get him. He'd be dead by next weekend.' With that she put her headphones on again and was lost in her music.

'How long have we been travelling?' asked Mum, peering out at the passing countryside. 'About 40 minutes', replied Dad. He continued driving on, looking very hard and mean.

Jessica was beside herself. With every second, the distance between them and her precious cat was increasing. Mum gave Dad 'that' look. He banged his hands down on the steering wheel, his face swollen and red with anger.

'I hope he is still there', whimpered Jess, as they drove back in stony silence.

Jess couldn't get out of the car fast enough when they finally pulled up at the beach cottage. She grabbed the keys and raced inside.

Sure enough there was the cat, still fast asleep on Jessica's bed, blissfully unaware that he now had only eight of his nine lives left!

Class discussion

1. What is your opinion about the title of this story?

    Do you think it is a suitable one?

    Before you read the story, what did you think it might be about?

    What are some of the reasons stories are given titles?

    Brainstorm other possible titles for this story.

    Write the title you like best. Don't forget to use capital letters where needed.

    _____

2. Are you familiar with the saying that 'cats have nine lives'?

    Brainstorm to list possible reasons why this expression is used.

Partner activity

Pets are very special. Tell your partner about a pet you have or had or would like to have. Don't forget its name, appearance, personality, history and actions.

Structure of a narrative

Structure

A narrative has:

A title:	Indicates what the story is about.	
	Attracts the attention of the reader.	
Orientation:	*Who*	Main character(s) and possible minor character(s).
	What	Initiating event that starts the story.
	Where	The setting or location.
	When	Time the story takes place.
Complication:	The problem which involves the main character(s).	
Resolution:	How the problem is solved.	
Conclusion:	How the story ends.	

1. Read the narrative *Home alone* again and answer the questions.

    Title   What is the title of the story? _____

    Orientation   Who were the characters in the story? _____

    _____

    What was the family doing? _____

    _____

Where are the family members? _____

_____

When did the story happen? _____

_____

Complication What was the problem? _____

_____

Resolution What did they decide to do? _____

_____

Conclusion How did the story end? _____

_____

Reading for information

1. True or false? Colour the correct answers.

   (a) Jessica's cat's name was Cheong. ○ **true** ○ **false**

   (b) Melissa didn't enjoy Dad's music. ○ **true** ○ **false**

   (c) The family would not be going back to their
   beach cottage for three weeks. ○ **true** ○ **false**

   (d) They had been travelling for a half an hour
   before they turned around and went back. ○ **true** ○ **false**

   (e) The cat was very frightened and concerned about being left behind. ○ **true** ○ **false**

Reading for understanding

1. Which sister do you think is older?

   _____

   Why do you think this?

   _____

   _____

   _____

   _____

2. How do you think Dad felt about having to
   go back for the cat?

   _____

   Explain why you think this.

   _____

   _____

   _____

   _____

   _____

3. There was 'stony silence' on the trip back. Why do you think each person was so quiet?
   What could each of them have been thinking?

   Dad:

   Mum:

   Melissa:

   Jessica:

4. Whose fault was it that the cat was left behind? _____

   Why? _____

   _____

Applying your knowledge

1. The family have been swimming, windsurfing and fishing at their beach cottage.
   Think of an activity that you would like to do if you were staying near the beach.
   Make a list of all the equipment you would use to do this activity.

   Activity: _____

   Equipment: _____

   _____

2. The family's car was cramped and overloaded. Add items to the list of things they could be
   taking home in their car and say what each is used for.

Item	Use
swimwear coolbox	swimming

1. Unjumble these words. They all have something to do with fishing.

    (a) taib _____   (b) ohok _____   (c) inel _____

    (d) ent _____   (e) ord _____   (f) skinre _____

Compound words

A compound word can be made by joining two smaller words.

For example: **windsurfer**   **wind + surfer**

                 overloaded   **over + loaded**

---

2. Make ten compound words from the narrative *Home alone* using one of these words and another word.

out	week	be	wind	any
country	loaf	head	over	her

_____   _____

_____   _____

_____   _____

_____   _____

_____   _____

3. Which word in the box:

find	(a) means the opposite of soft? _____
queried	(b) means choices? _____
loud	(c) means the opposite of lose? _____
second	(d) means the same as asked? _____
sister	(e) is a bed? _____
fast	(f) means the opposite of found? _____
lost	(g) means the opposite of brother? _____
left	(h) is a measure of time? _____
options	(i) means the opposite of slow? _____
bunk	(j) means the opposite of right? _____

Words to replace *said*

There are many words that can be used instead of the word **said**.
By using different words, it is possible to give more information about the speaker; for example, how he or she sounds or is feeling.

In *Home alone*	Jessica:	yelled, cried, whimpered
	Melissa:	queried, stated
	Mum:	remarked, asked

4. Choose a suitable word to replace 'said' in each sentence.

(a) 'Oh, no I can't believe it', said Peter.

(b) 'Watch out, it might bite', said Lucy.

(c) 'Put your shoes on now', said Dad.

(d) 'Why don't you want to go?' said the teacher.

Spelling

The days of the week

Can you spell the names of the seven days of the week?

Helpful hints

- You must start each word with a capital letter because it is a proper noun.
- The 'ur' sound is the same in Saturday and Thursday.
- If you say Wed – nes – day you will spell this word correctly.
- Monday has the word **on** in it. Think I will do it **on** Monday.
- The **ue** sound in Tuesday is made with two vowels. The **u** comes first.

Take a test. Your teacher may like to test these words or ask a partner to test you.

Check carefully. Write any word(s) you spelt incorrectly below. (Make sure that your spelling is correct this time.)

_____

_____

Find the helpful hint for word(s) that caused you difficulty and learn it.

Ask a partner to test that you can now spell the word(s) correctly.

Syllables

Longer words are easier to spell if broken into syllables. Syllables are parts of words with one vowel sound.

For example: **Mon/day**   has 2 syllables and 2 vowel sounds

Sat/ur/day   has 3 syllables and 3 vowel sounds

1.   Count the syllables in each word. You may find it helps if you clap the parts of the word and identify the vowel sounds.

Word	Syllables
January	
February	
March	
April	
May	
June	

Word	Syllables
July	
August	
September	
October	
November	
December	

Can you spell the months of the year? Read these hints before asking a partner to test you.

Jan/u/ar/y	If you say the four syllables you should be able to spell this word.
Feb/ru/ar/y	The difficult part of this word is the middle syllable 'ru' – Think 'kanga**roo**s run in Feb**ru**ary'.
March	One syllable, pretty easy to spell.
A/pril	Two syllables, say them clearly and it should be easy—A/pril.
May	No problem!
June	Think **u–e**. The letter **e** makes the long **u** sound.
Ju/ly	Two syllables—Ju/ly.
Au/gust	The first syllable is not a very common vowel sound. Think **autumn**, **auto**, **author**.
Sep/tem/ber	Three syllables, say them and the word is easy—Sep/tem/ber.
Oc/to/ber	Three syllables make it easy to spell.
No/vem/ber	Three easy syllables—No/vem/ber.
De/cem/ber	Three syllables, then the only difficulty is knowing the **s** sound is made with the letter **c**. Think 'Christmas'. If **c** is followed by **e**, **i** or **y,** the sound is soft.

Remember that the **er** sound is used in the months and **ur** is used in the days of the week.

*Different **er** sounds*

2. Circle the **er** sound in each word.

purple	*different*	*thirty*	*homework*
search	*journal*	*surprise*	*government*

3. Study the different ways of writing the same sound.

ir	er	ur	ear	or	our

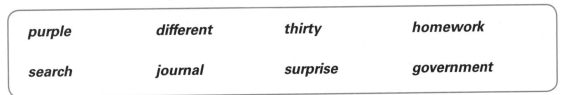

Select the correct one for each of the missing words.

(a) The comedian had a good sense of hum⬚.

(b) When they finished the netball game, the g⬚ls felt hot and th⬚sty.

(c) The inj⬚ed play⬚ needed s⬚g⬚y on his knee.

(d) Please come to school ⬚ly in the morning and l⬚n these w⬚ds.

(e) Put this money in your p⬚se to pay for your j⬚ney.

(f) Your w⬚k is wond⬚ful and w⬚th all the eff⬚t you put into it.

4. Work with a partner to add to these lists of words, which all have the same sound represented in different ways.

skirt	perch	burnt	worm	pearl

Adjectives

Adjectives are words used to describe people, places and things.

They can add to understanding about the appearance, personality or function (uses) of people, places and things.

For example: A **dry**, **sandy**, **deserted**, **beach** track.

The **short**, **stout**, **friendly**, **school-crossing** attendant.

1. Choose two adjectives to describe each of these people, places or things.

    (a) _____ , _____ cat

    (b) _____ , _____ vehicle

    (c) _____ , _____ sister

    (d) _____ , _____ road

    (e) _____ , _____ book

    (f) _____ , _____ journey

    (g) _____ , _____ accident

    (h) _____ , _____ game

2. How many of the 16 adjectives you wrote described:

    (a) appearance? ⬚   (b) personality? ⬚   (c) function? ⬚

Synonyms

Words that have the same or similar meaning are called **synonyms**.

For example: a **brave** act   a **courageous** act

3. Underline the adjective and write a synonym for each.

    (a) a little girl   _____   (b) a huge elephant _____

    (c) a selfish friend   _____   (d) a dirty shoe   _____

    (e) a wonderful holiday _____   (f) a useful tool   _____

    (g) hot water   _____   (h) a fantastic book _____

    (i) an interesting hat   _____   (j) a tasty pizza   _____

    (k) new computer   _____   (l) a warm coat   _____

    (m) a nasty cold   _____   (n) a helpful teacher _____

Design a poster

4. (a) Design a poster describing a **missing pet**.

Remember to give information about its appearance, personality, where it was last seen and, of course, what people with information should do.

(b) Highlight or underline the adjectives on your poster. Remember, the more detailed the information you provide, the more likely it is that someone will recognise your pet.

Adding adjectives

5. (a) Rewrite this short passage, adding appropriate adjectives to the bold nouns (naming words).

> The **duck** swam around the **lake** looking for **food**.
> Her **babies** followed her, making **noises**.

_____

_____

_____

_____

_____

_____

    (b) How many adjectives did you add?

    (c) Is the passage more interesting now? ◯ **yes** ◯ **no**

Commas

Commas are used to separate items or adjectives.

> For example: The family saw horses, sheep, goats, sheds,
> windmills, houses, paddocks, fences and
> gates on their way to the farm.

Did you notice that there is no comma between the last two items? This is because of the word **and**.

---

6. Use commas to punctuate these sentences.

    (a) The old dilapidated wooden gate won't close.

    (b) My cute lively friendly soft and cuddly kitten is hiding.

    (c) I've lost my new blue and white school jumper.

    (d) The fast noisy red racing car sped around the track.

    (e) Jill is a horrible rude selfish young girl.

7. Write two sentences using lists and commas.

(a) In my cupboard I keep _____

_____

_____

(b) On the weekend I _____

_____

_____

_____

Commas are used when you need a pause in a sentence to make it easier to understand. For example: After we cleaned our teeth and had a shower, we went to bed.

8. Add commas to these sentences.

(a) Before you go to bed make sure that your teeth have been cleaned.

(b) Last Friday after school our teacher took us to see a film.

(c) After you've been for a swim and had a shower remember to hang up your swimsuit.

(d) I've invited my friends Jarrad Tom Craig and Dale to come on a picnic so I hope it won't rain.

WRITING Activities

A narrative = characters + complication + resolution

Characters: Good writers make their characters seem real. We usually know their appearance, personality and likely actions.

Complication: Readers need to understand the problems faced by the main character(s).

Resolution: The resolution must develop from the situation confronting the main character(s), be believable and relate to the personality of the character(s) involved.

Characters

1. (a) Personality scale

    What do you know about Jessica and Melissa's dad? Place a cross on the scale to indicate your opinion of their dad's personality.

    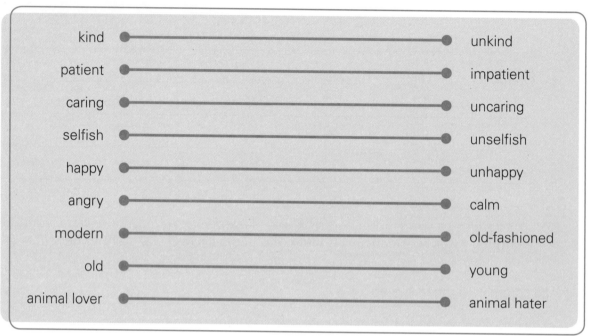

    kind — unkind

    patient — impatient

    caring — uncaring

    selfish — unselfish

    happy — unhappy

    angry — calm

    modern — old-fashioned

    old — young

    animal lover — animal hater

    (b) Discuss each of their dad's personality traits with a partner and justify your decisions.

    (c) Write a short passage describing their dad. Choose a suitable title. Remember, a title should reflect your ideas and must interest the reader. (Don't forget the capital letters.)

    _____

    _____

    _____

    _____

    _____

    (d) How does your father or a father you know well rate? Use a coloured pencil to rate him on the same personality scale.

    (e) Write 10 adjectives to describe this man. You can select words about his appearance and personality.

    (f) Write 10 verbs (doing words) to tell about his actions. For example: he gardens, surfs, growls.

Writing resolutions

- Resolutions that are satisfying to the reader must develop out of the situation confronting the main character.

- The action taken must also relate to the personality of the character involved.

- Stories can have two possible endings.

1.

The ending the reader **hopes** will happen (... and the woodcutter saved Little Red Riding Hood).

2.

The ending the reader **fears** will happen (... and the wolf ate Little Red Riding Hood).

Tips for writing resolutions

Do:

1. make certain the main character works out the solution.

2. create suspense by keeping the characters from reaching their goal too easily or quickly.

3. create additional difficulties; that is, have more than one attempt to solve the problem.

Don't:

1. depend on coincidence to solve the problem. (Bill just 'finds' a gun in his pocket.)

2. introduce a new character to save the day.

3. have the main character announce 'And then I woke from a dream'.

2. Think about the resolution in *Home alone*. They resolved the complication in this story by turning around and going back for the cat.

(a) Did the main character(s) work out the solution? ◯ **yes** ◯ **no**

(b) Did they turn around immediately and was there some suspense created? ◯ **yes** ◯ **no**

(c) Were there some additional difficulties? ◯ **yes** ◯ **no**

(d) Did they solve the problem with some amazing coincidence? ◯ **yes** ◯ **no**

(e) Was a new character introduced who saved the day? ◯ **yes** ◯ **no**

(f) Did they all wake up from a dream and find their problem wasn't real? ◯ **yes** ◯ **no**

The English workbook **63**

Home alone has been analysed using a narrative plan. Study this to help you understand the different parts of a narrative.

Title	Home alone
Orientation	
Characters	Jessica – young, bored, hysterical, worried, soft-hearted Mum – calm, tolerant Dad – angry, bossy, impatient Melissa – loves music, logical, clear thinking Cheong – sleepy, unaware
Setting/Location	The country, in a car
Time	Summer
Initiating event	
What event starts the action?	Mum asks if they have their cat.
How does this involve the characters?	They have to make a decision.
Complication	
What problem do the characters have?	Should they go back to their beach cottage?
What caused the problem?	The cat is back at their beach cottage.
Resolution	
How is the problem solved?	They turn around and go back.
Conclusion	
What happened in the end?	They find the cat fast asleep on the bed.

1. (a) Use your imagination to complete the narrative plan that has been started for you. Don't forget the title. The resolution should come naturally from the story.

Title	
Orientation	
Characters	Shane – 10 years old, responsible, resourceful, helpful Sue – 6 years old, silly, careless, dependent Surfboarders – wave chasers Other beach goers – swimmers, walkers
Setting/location	The beach
Time	Summer
Initiating event	
What event starts the action?	Sue starts crying because she's dropped her beach ball.
How does this involve the characters?	Shane tries to help her.
Complication	
What problem do the characters have?	Her beach ball has blown into the water.
What caused the problem?	The wind is very strong.
Resolution	
How is the problem solved?	
Conclusion	
What happened in the end?	

(b) Write the story on a separate sheet of paper, using your plan as a guide.

Choose a topic from the box below and write a narrative. Use the plan to guide your ideas. When you are ready, write the story in full. Try to make your characters believable.

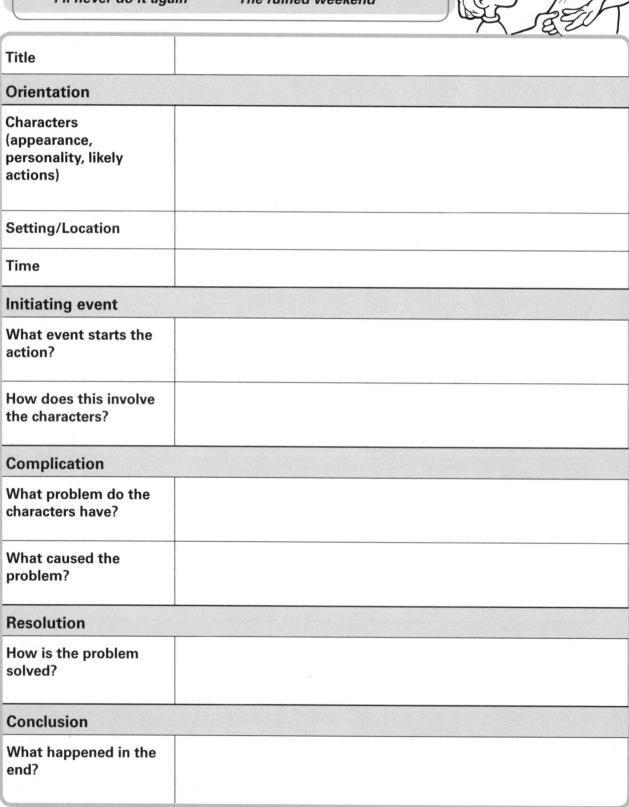

Sisters are a menace	*A lucky pet*
Cats need nine lives	*The horrible holiday*
I'll never do it again	*The ruined weekend*

Title	
Orientation	
Characters (appearance, personality, likely actions)	
Setting/Location	
Time	
Initiating event	
What event starts the action?	
How does this involve the characters?	
Complication	
What problem do the characters have?	
What caused the problem?	
Resolution	
How is the problem solved?	
Conclusion	
What happened in the end?	

When you have completed your story, proofread and edit it using the following questions as a guide.

Checklist

Title of the narrative

1. Title

(a) Does the title indicate what the story is about?.............................. ⚪ **yes** ⚪ **no**

(b) Does it get the attention of the reader? .... ⚪ **yes** ⚪ **no**

2. Orientation

(a) Does the beginning draw the reader into the characters' world?.... ⚪ **yes** ⚪ **no**

(b) Are the characters believable? .... ⚪ **yes** ⚪ **no**

(c) Do their actions fit their personalities?... ⚪ **yes** ⚪ **no**

(d) Is the setting realistic? .... ⚪ **yes** ⚪ **no**

3. Initiating event

Is the problem known at the beginning of the story?.............................. ⚪ **yes** ⚪ **no**

4. Complication

Is the problem believable?... ⚪ **yes** ⚪ **no**

5. Resolution

(a) Does the resolution fit the complication?...................................... ⚪ **yes** ⚪ **no**

(b) Have the problems been solved? .... ⚪ **yes** ⚪ **no**

6. Conclusion

Is the ending satisfying to the reader? .... ⚪ **yes** ⚪ **no**

7. Punctuation and spelling

Have you checked the following?

(a) Spelling – use a dictionary or ask someone .... ⚪ **yes** ⚪ **no**

(b) Punctuation – including capital letters, full stops,
question marks, commas and direct speech. .... ⚪ **yes** ⚪ **no**

(c) Paragraphs for new ideas.. ⚪ **yes** ⚪ **no**

8. Vocabulary

(a) Have you used some interesting adjectives? .... ⚪ **yes** ⚪ **no**

(b) Have you used any compound words? .... ⚪ **yes** ⚪ **no**

(c) Have you used more interesting verbs instead of **said**?.............. ⚪ **yes** ⚪ **no**

1. Choose a title from the box and plan, then write, a narrative on a separate sheet of paper.

The lost pet	**A wonderful holiday**	**A lucky escape**
A disastrous day	**Welcome home**	**Only eight lives left**

2. (a) A narrative has these parts: a t_____, an orientation, a

      c_____, a r_____ and a c_____.

   (b) The orientation tells who, _____, _____ and when.

   (c) The resolution tells how the problem is _____.

   (d) The conclusion tells _____.

3. Use these words to make five compound words.

brush	**him**	**surfer**	**tooth**	**one**
wind	**any**	**every**	**body**	**self**

   _____

4. Choose a suitable word to replace **said** in each sentence.

   (a) 'Do it now!' Dad said.   (b) 'Why can't I come?' said his little brother.

   _____   _____

   (c) Mum said, 'Please be ready at 4 o'clock'. (d) 'I've looked all over for my shoes', said Ben.

   _____   _____

5. Spell these days of the week.

   (a) The day that starts with **W**.   (b) The day that starts with **Th**.

   _____   _____

   (c) The two days starting with the letter **S**. (d) The day that starts with **M**

   _____ and   _____

   _____

6. Spell these months of the year.

   (a) The month after January.   (b) The last month of the year.

   _____   _____

   (c) The month before October.   (d) The month after July.

   _____   _____

7. Circle the **er** sound in each word.

   (a) worth   (b) shirt   (c) churn   (d) colour

   (e) heard   (f) surprise   (g) research   (h) virtual

8. Choose two suitable adjectives for each of these.

   (a) the _____, _____ car

   (b) the _____, _____ jumper

   (c) the _____, _____ swimmer

   (d) the _____, _____ holiday

9. Write a synonym for each adjective.

   (a) A horrible accident

   (b) The last act

   (c) The largest ship

   (d) The revolting mess

10. Rewrite the short passage adding suitable adjectives to each of the bold nouns (naming words).

    The **dog** barked loudly when the **man** approached the **house** and began to climb in the window.

    _____

    _____

    _____

11. Use commas to punctuate these sentences.

    (a) It was a long hot dusty road.

    (b) They noticed some large noisy black crows.

    (c) The small grey frightened kangaroo jumped away.

    (d) After the family reached their beach cottage they unpacked the car.

    (e) Their cat Cheong was asleep on the bed.

    (f) The clear calm blue ocean looked very inviting.

    (g) Before they all got into the car Dad checked to make sure the front door was locked.

Spotted tree frogs

Reports give **facts** clearly **without unnecessary information** or **opinions**.

Read this report about the spotted tree frog.

Spotted tree frogs

The Australian spotted tree frog, whose scientific name is *Litoria spenceri*, is an endangered amphibian.

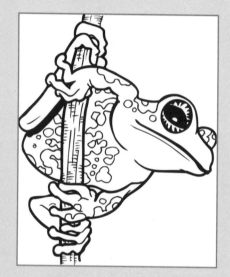

The male grows to about 60 mm long, with the female being slightly larger (up to 61 mm).

The frog varies from brown, grey or olive-green to bright green, sometimes with brown or darker spots and small warts on its back. Under its belly, it may have a pale orange colour towards the back and behind the limbs. Its toes and fingers are flat and the sticky discs on its toes allow it to cling to vertical surfaces like rocks and tree trunks. The frog's large eyes have horizontal pupils.

Spotted tree frogs reproduce from October to December. The female lays up to 1000 eggs, in narrow spaces between the river stones.

The frog's habitat is cold, swift-flowing mountain streams, usually in very steep, rocky areas ranging from dense, moist forests at higher altitudes to more open areas at lower altitudes. The frog can be found from the Central Highlands of Victoria to Mt Kosciuszko in New South Wales.

Adults feed on flying insects, especially mosquitoes and flies, while the tadpoles feed on algae. The frogs drink water from the streams.

Because there are only approximately 4000 individual frogs remaining in about 12 isolated populations, the species has been listed under the *Environment Protection and Biodiversity Conservation Act 1999*. The reason for the decline in numbers is unknown, but it is thought to be related to the introduction of trout species, which feed on the tadpoles, and also habitat disturbances, affecting water quality and increasing sediment. Disease and forest fires may also play a part.

The spotted tree frog will not survive for future generations unless it is protected.

Class activity

1. Make a list of words you could use to describe frogs.

2. There are many stories featuring frogs. Compile a list of books or stories about frogs or well-known frog characters.

Partner activity

3. (a)   Choose one frog character you like and write its name (or the book it is from) on the line.

    (b)   In the boxes below, write three words to describe your frog.

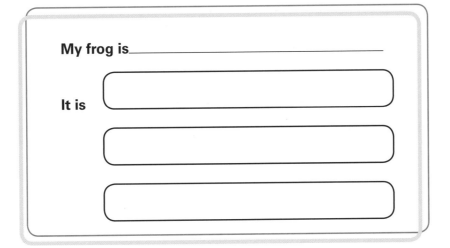

My frog is _____

It is

    (c)   Explain to your partner why you chose this frog.

Structure of a report

Structure

This report has:

A title:	Tells what the report is about.
Orientation:	What is it? Gives information about the focus of the report.
Description:	Features: What it looks like
	Where it lives
	What it does
Conclusion:	A summary or comment.

Reread the report *Spotted tree frog* and answer the questions.

1. **Title**   What is the title of this report? _____

2. **Classification** To what species of animal does the
                      spotted tree frog (*Litoria spenceri*) belong? _____

3. **Description**   What size is it? _____

                      What colour is it? _____

                      _____

                      What are its eyes like? _____

                      _____

                      When and where does it reproduce? _____

                      _____

                      Where does it live? _____

                      _____

                      What does it eat? _____

                      _____

                      Why is it endangered? _____

                      _____

4. **Conclusion**   What is the writer concerned about? _____

                      _____

Reading for information

1. True or false? Colour the correct answers.

   (a) The male spotted tree frog is bigger than the female.   ◯ **true** ◯ **false**

   (b) Some spotted tree frogs have warts on their backs.   ◯ **true** ◯ **false**

   (c) They lay their eggs between river stones.   ◯ **true** ◯ **false**

   (d) Spotted tree frogs are found in Tasmania.   ◯ **true** ◯ **false**

   (e) Trout eat tadpoles.   ◯ **true** ◯ **false**

Reading for understanding

1. What are two things that people could do to protect spotted tree frogs?

_____

_____

2. (a) Why do you think people put trout into the rivers?

(b) Why are trout affecting the numbers of spotted tree frogs?

3. Why do you think these spotted frogs are called spotted *tree* frogs?

_____

Applying your knowledge

Draw a diagram showing the different stages in the life cycle of the spotted tree frog. Label your diagram clearly.

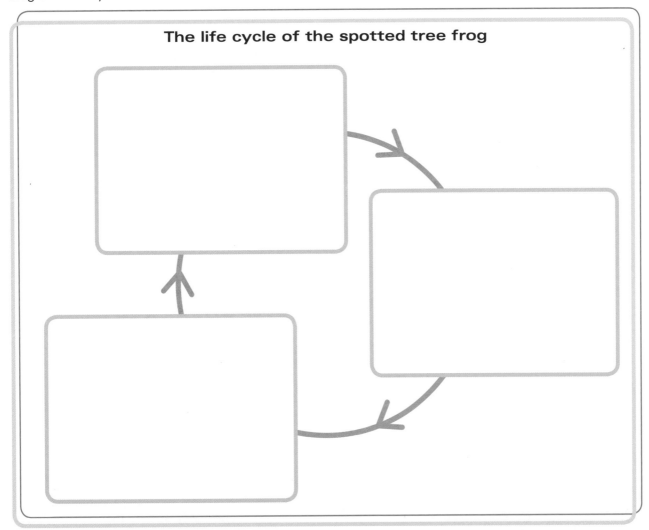

The life cycle of the spotted tree frog

1. (a) Categorise the words below. You may need to refer to an encyclopedia or dictionary for some of them.

   (b) Add some to each list.

   > toad, emu, lizard, whale, seahorse, crocodile, duck, platypus,
   > shark, bat, frog, sea snake, pelican, salamander

fish	bird	amphibian	reptile	mammal

2. What am I?

   (a) I have a bill like a duck and a flat tail.

   I lay eggs and burrow into riverbanks.

   I am a _____.

   (b) I am large and I live in the sea.

   I feed my young on milk.

   I am a _____.

   (c) I am nocturnal and I have wings.

   I do not lay eggs.

   I am a _____.

   (d) Write a 'What am I?' for a friend to solve.

   _____

   _____

   I am a _____.

3. (a) Find an animal starting with each letter of the alphabet.

(a)	(b)	(c)
(d)	(e)	(f)
(g)	(h)	(i)
(j)	(k)	(l)
(m)	(n)	(o)
(p)	(q)	(r)
(s)	(t)	(u)
(v)	(w)	(x)
(y)	(z)	

(b) Which letter or letters couldn't you find an animal for?

4. Circle the odd one out and write a sentence to explain your choice.

(a) **bear**   **tiger**   **whale**   **crocodile**   **kangaroo**

_____

_____

(b) **snake**   **bat**   **goose**   **swan**   **frog**

_____

_____

(c) **emu**   **robin**   **magpie**   **parrot**   **wren**

_____

_____

(d) **snake**   **shark**   **horse**   **seahorse**   **dolphin**

_____

_____

(e) **lizard**   **turtle**   **snake**   **crocodile**   **toad**

_____

_____

Plurals

Spelling the plurals of some words in English can be a challenge, but the first and most common way is simply to add the letter **s**.

For example: bird – bird**s**   frog – frog**s**

Learn the following rules, but remember there are often exceptions to every rule.

Rule

Nouns ending in **x**, **s**, **z**, **ch** or **sh** add **es** to make the plural easier to say.

For example:

box – box**es**

church – church**es**

Note: If the **ch** makes a **k** sound, just add **s**.

For example:

monar**chs**, stoma**chs**

Rule

Nouns ending in **f** or **fe** change the **f** or **fe** to **v**, then add **es**.

For example:

wife – wi**ves**   half – hal**ves**

Note: There are some exceptions.

For example: chefs, beliefs, reefs, chiefs

For some words, both spellings are accepted.

For example:

dwarf**s**, dwar**ves**

hoof**s**, hoo**ves**   scar**f**, scar**ves**

Advice: Consult a dictionary if you are unsure.

---

1.   Write the plurals of these words. They all follow the rules you have learnt.

	Singular	Plural			Singular	Plural
(a)	loaf		(b)	arch		
(c)	circus		(d)	gas		
(e)	house		(f)	fax		
(g)	novel		(h)	thief		
(i)	brush		(j)	virus		
(k)	calf		(l)	camel		
(m)	fox		(n)	suffix		
(o)	waltz		(p)	branch		
(q)	bus		(r)	dish		

Crazy pictures

2. (a) Underline the plurals in the sentence below.
    (b) Draw the picture in the space provided.

> The crazy wives made their hungry husbands some sandwiches with pickles, radishes and carrots, then tried to cut them into halves using blunt knives.

(c) Make up a crazy sentence using at least six plurals. Underline the plurals you have used. Ask a partner to draw your crazy picture on a separate sheet of paper.

_____

_____

_____

_____

(d) How many plurals did you use? _____

(e) How many just have 's' added? _____

(f) How many followed the rules you learnt? _____

3. Write the singular of each bold noun in the space provided.

(a) The family left the **brushes** (_____) and **combs** (_____)

on the **shelves** (_____).

(b) The **buses** (_____) took the **boys** (_____) and **girls**

(_____) across the **marshes** (_____) to visit the local

schools (_____).

(c) The **pirates** (_____) should find buried **treasures** (_____)

on the **islands** (_____).

(d) The **glasses** (_____) fell off the **benches** (_____) because

the strong wind blew the **doors** (_____) open.

Prepositions

A proposition connects one thing with another, showing how they are related.

Prepositions can tell about **place** or **time**.

1. Read these sentences. The prepositions are bold. Write **place** or **time** under each sentence.

   (a) There is an old building **on** the hill.

   _____

   (b) Mum always keeps her glasses **in** the drawer.

   _____

   (c) We always clean our teeth **before** going to bed.

   _____

   (d) Trees lose their leaves **during** autumn.

   _____

   (e) Dad gets home **about** six every night.

   _____

   (f) People are waiting **at** the bus stop.

   _____

2. Use a preposition from the box to complete each sentence.

while	through	without
outside	around	after

   (a) Her shoes were left

   _____ the door.

   (b) The cyclists rode _____ the park.

   (c) You can't play in the sun

   _____ a hat.

   (d) _____ we were working, the telephone rang.

   (e) The bees buzzed _____ the flowers.

   (f) We watched TV _____ dinner.

3. Circle the correct prepositions.

   (a) Mum growled (at, with) me for breaking the glass.

   (b) The packet is full (of, with) biscuits.

   (c) We'll sit here and wait (for, after) Sarah.

   (d) She is well qualified (with, for) the position.

   (e) The nurse cared (after, for) the patients.

   (f) I'm not afraid (at, of) the dark.

4. Use each word as a preposition in a sentence about frogs. Try to make your sentences interesting.

(a) around

(b) under

(c) with

(d) until

(e) past

5. Circle the preposition in each sentence.

(a) The plane is flying above the clouds.

(b) There is an amusing programme on television.

(c) Breakfast is served from seven o'clock.

(d) Please return your library books by Friday.

(e) A lot of houses lost their roofs during the storm.

(f) How did the thief break into the house?

WRITING Activities

Facts and opinions

Reports contain **facts** (true statements) and not **opinions** (what the author thinks).

1. Write **fact** or **opinion** after each sentence.

(a) Birds lay eggs. _____

(b) Birds are beautiful. _____

(c) Magpies are black and white. _____

(d) Magpies are horrible because they attack people who approach their nests. _____

(e) Birdwatching is interesting. _____

2. Choose one animal from the box below. Write three **facts** and three **opinions** about it.

| dolphins | crocodiles | cows | geese | eagles | zebras |

Facts about

1. _____

_____

2. _____

_____

3. _____

_____

Opinions about

1. _____

_____

2. _____

_____

3. _____

_____

Reports give facts clearly, without unnecessary information.

Good report writers are able to choose the most relevant or important facts and write them clearly.

Read this report about elephants.

Elephants

Elephants are large mammals; they are the biggest animals living on land today.

Their skin is grey and very thick. They use their huge ears to keep themselves cool.

The elephant's trunk is amazing. It is used for reaching high branches, drinking, transferring food, bathing and detecting danger.

Its enormous upper teeth are in the form of tusks, used for obtaining food and for fighting.

The two remaining species are the Asian and the African. Asian elephants are smaller and easier to train. African elephants have larger ears, needed for cooling themselves.

Elephants are herbivores, eating grasses, leaves, twigs and fruit.

Working elephants have been used in Asia for hundreds of years to clear forests, provide transport, and move logs. They often feature in parades.

Young elephants take two years to develop after birth and they are dependent on their mother's milk for three years.

Keywords

1. (a) Choose eight important words from the report and write them below.
   Hint: By looking at the eight keywords you should be able to decide what the report is about.

   _____   _____   _____   _____

   _____   _____   _____   _____

   (b) Compare your eight words with a partner. Were your words the same?   ◯ **yes** ◯ **no**

   (c) Discuss with your partner why you chose your words. Work together to choose the four most important words.

   _____   _____   _____   _____

2. (a) Find the four most important facts from the report and write them below.

   • _____

   _____

   • _____

   _____

   • _____

   _____

   • _____

   _____

   (b) Compare your four facts with your partner and discuss the similarities and differences. Work out which two facts you both agree are the most important ones.

Fact	Fact

Choose a topic for a report from the box below and use the plan to prepare it before writing it in full on a separate sheet of paper. Remember to use facts not opinions. You may need to research to find some important facts.

monkeys	rabbits	cheetahs	toads
beetles	lions	lizards	ladybirds

Title:

Classification (Type): _____

_____

Description:

> *What do they look like?*

> *Where do they live?*

> *What do they do?*

> *What they eat?*

> *Any other important facts?*

Conclusion: _____

_____

After you have written your report in full, use the checklist below to edit your work.

You will self-editing for:

Spelling   Punctuation

Grammar   Sentence structure

You will be using a peer editor to:

Check sense

Check that you have used facts

Checklist

Title of report: _____

1. Does your report include information about:

   (a) what they look like?.. ◯ **yes** ◯ **no**

   (b) where they live? .... ◯ **yes** ◯ **no**

   (c) what they do?... ◯ **yes** ◯ **no**

   (d) what they eat? .... ◯ **yes** ◯ **no**

   (e) any other important facts? .... ◯ **yes** ◯ **no**

2. Have you written facts, not opinions? .... ◯ **yes** ◯ **no**

3. Do you have a concluding statement?......................... ◯ **yes** ◯ **no**

4. Have you corrected any spelling errors?..................... ◯ **yes** ◯ **no**

5. Have you used capital letters and full stops correctly? .... ◯ **yes** ◯ **no**

6. Did your peer editor:

   (a) understand your report?
        ◯ **yes** ◯ **no**

   (b) believe your facts are true?
        ◯ **yes** ◯ **no**

1. Choose a topic from the box below and write a report on a separate sheet of paper. Use a report plan to help you organise your ideas.

| snakes | spiders | scorpions |
| whales | bears | tigers |

2. Complete the following statements:

    (a) Reports give _____

    _____

    (b) Structure of a report:
    A report has:

    | a title | cl |
    | d | co |

    (c) A report should give _____ not opinions.

3. Write the plurals of these words.

    (a) lion _____

    (b) fox _____

    (c) lunch _____

    (d) dress _____

    (e) waltz _____

    (f) table _____

    (g) wish _____

    (h) gas _____

    (i) pilot _____

    (j) march _____

4. Write **time** or **place** for each preposition in these sentences.

    (a) We visited the old castle **on** the hill.

    (b) **While** the girl was waiting for the bus, it began to rain.

    (c) **During** the holidays, the children played with their friends.

    (d) The packages were left **outside** our front door.

    (e) Clean your teeth **after** you've had dinner.

    (f) I left my sports bag **under** the seat of Mum's car.

5. Use a proposition from the box to complete each sentence.

after	beside	without	through

(a) The tourists strolled _____ the museum.

(b) We stood _____ the statue in the park.

(c) _____ our dinner, we watched TV.

(d) The bus left _____ him because he was late.

6. Circle the correct proposition.

(a) The apples fell (off, from) the tree.

(b) Ben jumped (off, into) the pool.

(c) We'll meet at the gate and wait (after, for) Tim.

(d) He sat (between, among) the two girls.

7. Use each preposition in a sentence.

(a) over

(b) by

8. Circle the preposition in each sentence.

(a) The library is closed between 1300 and 1400.

(b) He doesn't like going to the dentist.

(c) After the party, we all went home.

(d) It rained while we were waiting for the bus.

9. Are these **facts** or **opinions**?

(a) Elephants have tusks they use for obtaining food. .... ◯ **fact** ◯ **opinion**

(b) They like to fight. .... ◯ **fact** ◯ **opinion**

(c) Young elephants enjoy staying with their mothers. .... ◯ **fact** ◯ **opinion**

(d) Elephants eat grass, leaves and fruit. .... ◯ **fact** ◯ **opinion**

Grass head

The purpose of a procedure is to **direct**, **inform** or **explain** how to do something.

Read the procedure.

Grass head

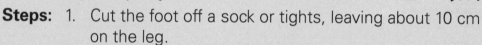

You will need: Old sock or pair of tights (must be thin)
Scissors
Grass seeds
Potting mix
Cotton thread or string
Elastic band
Felt scraps
Fabric glue
Paper cup or jar

Steps:
1. Cut the foot off a sock or tights, leaving about 10 cm on the leg.
2. Put a handful of grass seeds into the toe and press down firmly.
3. Fill the remainder of the toe with potting mix (about the size of a tennis ball).
4. Tie the end of the sock with cotton thread or string.
5. Form a nose by pulling out a section and tying an elastic band to hold the shape.
6. Cut out eyes and mouth from scraps of felt.
7. Glue them into place.
8. When dry, sit the head on top of a paper cup or jar filled with water.

Enjoy watching the grass hair grow!

Speaking and listening

Class activity

1. Brainstorm different purposes for cultivating plants; for example: preventing soil erosion, furniture manufacturing.

Partner activity

2. Choose one purpose for plant cultivation from the class list to discuss with a partner. Decide on five important facts about plant cultivation for this purpose. Share your information with the class.

> **herbivores   carnivores   omnivores**

3. (a) Discuss what each of the above terms means and list examples.

    (b) Which category do you belong to? _____

    (c) Does your partner belong to the same category? ○ **yes** ○ **no**

Class activity

4. (a) There are many people who choose to be vegetarians. Brainstorm some of the advantages and disadvantages.

    (b) Record your opinions.

I think the most persuasive argument for being a vegetarian is	I think the most persuasive argument against being a vegetarian is

Structure of a procedure

Structure

This procedure has:

A goal: Tells what is to be done

Requirements: Items needed to complete a task

Steps: A list, usually in order of what to do.

Test: Was the task completed successfully?

1.   Read the procedure for making a grass head and answer the questions.

Goal

What is the goal or purpose of this procedure?

Requirements

What is required to complete the task?

Steps

In which order would you complete these tasks? Colour or highlight the one you would do first.

Cut out the eyes.	OR	Press the seed into the sock.
Fill the toe with potting mix.	OR	Leave 10 cm on the leg.
Sit the head on a cup.	OR	Tie the sock with cotton thread.
Form a nose.	OR	Watch the grass grow.
Cut a mouth from scraps.	OR	Cut off the foot of the sock.

Test

How would you know if this procedure was successful?

_____

_____

_____

WORKING WITH THE TEXT   **Reading**

Reading for information

1.   True or false? Colour the correct answer.

(a)   The potting mix is placed in the sock before the grass seeds.   ◯ **true** ◯ **false**

(b)   The eyes, mouth and nose are made of felt.   ◯ **true** ◯ **false**

(c)   A teaspoonful of grass seeds is needed.   ◯ **true** ◯ **false**

(d)   An elastic band is used for the nose.   ◯ **true** ◯ **false**

(e)   The jar must be filled with water before placing the head on top of it.   ◯ **true** ◯ **false**

Reading for understanding

1. Is it important to follow the steps of this procedure in the correct order?　○ **yes** ○ **no**

   Why/Why not? _____

   _____

   _____

2. Are the instructions clear?

   ○ **yes** ○ **no**

   Could you make a grass head without assistance?

   ○ **yes** ○ **no**

3. Why must the glue be dry before placing the grass head on the paper cup or jar?

4. Why does the paper cup or jar need to be filled with water?

   _____

   _____

   _____

   _____

5. How long do you think the grass seeds will take to grow?

   _____

6. Why do you think it is called a 'grass head'?

   _____

   _____

Applying your knowledge

1. List some things that plants need to grow.

2. Not all grass heads will look the same. Why?

   _____

   _____

3. What age group do you think would enjoy this activity?_____

   Why?_____

   _____

4. (a) What is your favourite plant? _____

    Give three reasons for your choice.

    (b) Design a poster to persuade people to value this plant.

Base words

Base words are parts of words based on words from other languages.

For example: **centi** – from Latin, meaning one hundred.
centipede, **cent**ury

1. Some common Greek or Latin bases are listed below. Use a dictionary or the Internet to find out if they came from the Greek or Latin language and give two examples from the English language. The first one has been done.

Base word	Language of origin	Meaning	Words using the base word	
cent	Latin	one hundred	centipede	century
aqua				
bio				
omni				
photo				
tele				
geo				
cardio				

Find the hidden words

2. Cross out the letters **p**, **d**, **f** and **u**. Write the letters that are left on the line below. Can you read the words? They are all **similes**.

(a) **dfapusfdgprfeuednfpadsfugfrpaupsdfspu**

_____

(b) **dafpsudbfpluacfpkadduspdifufnpkud**

_____

(c) **fpaudsfpuwdfhiptufdepuapffssdunfopwd**

_____

(d) **puafsudtfphuidnuafsupaurfdaukpe**

_____

(e) **fapdfsupsfulpofwufapdsfuaptdpodrptufodipsfeu**

_____

Similes compare one thing with another, using the words **as** or **like**.

Some **similes** you may have heard are:

- swims like a fish
- as cunning as a fox
- as strong as an ox

3. Write some other **similes** you have heard.

(a) _____

(b) _____

(c) _____

(d) _____

(e) _____

Spelling

Suffixes

A suffix is a group of letters attached to the end of a word.

For example: **ing, ed, er, ern, est, ly, ful**.

There are many spelling rules for adding a suffix, but it is usually just added to the word.

For example: look**ing**, jump**ed**, cold**er**, west**ern**, great**est**, like**ly**, thank**ful**.

Rule:

To add **ly** to words ending in **le** after a **consonant** change the **e** to **y**.

For example: simpl**e** – simpl**y**.

1. Use this rule to add the suffix **ly** to these words.

(a)	horrible	horribly	(b)	visible	
(c)	idle		(d)	probable	
(e)	feeble		(f)	terrible	
(g)	capable		(h)	comfortable	

Rule: If **le** follows a vowel, just add **ly** to the word.
For example: sole – solely
Note: An exception is whole – wholly.

2. Add **ly** to these words. They all end in **le**, some after consonants, some after vowels.

(a)	suitable	(b)	knowledgeable
(c)	pale	(d)	vile
(e)	futile	(f)	subtle
(g)	noticeable	(h)	forcible
(i)	noble	(j)	responsible

Rule: To add **ly** to words ending in **y** when the **y** makes an **e** sound, the **e** is changed to **i** before adding **ly**. For example: speed**y** – speed**ily**

3. Use the above rule to add **ly** to the bold words.

(a) He ate the food **greedy**. _____

(b) The man trod **heavy** on the path. _____

(c) He won his race **easy**. _____

(d) Brett **happy** stayed on the computer all day. _____

(e) We packed the books **tidy** into boxes. _____

4. Add **ly** to these words. Remember: Only change the **y** to **i** when the **y** makes an **e** sound.

(a) shy _____   (b) busy _____

(c) clumsy _____   (d) sly _____

(e) mighty _____   (f) weary _____

Rule: When words end in **ac** or **ic**, always add **k** before adding **ed**, **er**, **ing** and **y**.
For example: panic – panicked, panicking, panicky.

5. Add the suffixes.

	Word	ed	er	ing	y
(a)	picnic				
(b)	colic				
(c)	plastic				
(d)	mimic				
(e)	traffic				

Adverbs

Adverbs are words which can add meaning to verbs. They can tell where, when or how something happens.

> For example:
>
> | | |
> |---|---|
> | Adverbs of place (where) | near, outside, behind, above |
> | Adverbs of time (when) | yesterday, later, seldom, today |
> | Adverbs of manner (how) | slowly, smoothly, beautifully |

    when   verb   how

Yesterday my friend **broke** his arm **badly**.

1. Underline the verb, then circle the adverb in each sentence.

   (a) He ran outside.

   (b) My uncle took me to the beach yesterday.

   (c) My sunburnt back hurt badly.

   (d) Tomorrow is my birthday.

   (e) I jumped quickly into the swimming pool.

2. Choose an adverb from the box to tell **how**, **when** or **where** these things happened.

early	*strongly*	*today*	*loudly*	*outside*

   (a) Even though I yelled _____, my brother could not hear me. (*how*)

   (b) My poor mother had to get up _____ to drive my brother to swimming training. (*when*)

   (c) I left my bike _____. (*where*)

   (d) She swam _____ to win the race. (*how*)

   (e) _____ is my birthday. (*when*)

3. Write sentences using these adverbs of place. (*where*)

   (a) behind

   (b) outside

   (c) everywhere

4. Write sentences using these adverbs of time. (*when*)

(a) never

(b) frequently

(c) before

5. Write sentences using these adverbs of manner. (*how*)

(a) hopefully

(b) bravely

(c) curiously

6. Replace the bold words with an adverb from the box.

| *sadly* | *inside* | *yesterday* | *loudly* | *today* |

(a) She finished eating all her Easter eggs **the day before today.** _____

(b) We have sport **the day it is now**.   _____

(c) When he cut his foot he yelled **making lots of noise**.   _____

(d) The children cried **in a sad way**.   _____

(e) There are lots of flowers **not outside**.   _____

Adjectives to adverbs

7. Change the following words (adjectives) to **adverbs** by adding suffixes. You may need to revise the spelling rules on pages 92–93. For example: pain – painfully.

(a) curious

(b) stupid

(c) comfortable

(d) sensible

(e) understandable

(f) careful

(g) famous

WRITING   **Review procedures**

Read the procedure *Grass head* again and answer the following questions.

Text organisation

1. What is the goal? _____

_____

2. Is the order of the steps important? _____

Why? _____

_____

Language features

3. Why is it important that clear, concise statements are used in procedures?

_____

_____

4. What should you do if you don't understand what to do next in a procedure?

_____

_____

_____

Procedures use clear, concise language and often include command verbs.

1. Circle the command verb in each sentence.

   (a) Turn off the tap.

   (b) Keep to the left.

   (c) When turning, slow down.

   (d) Watch out for trains.

   (e) Before eating, wash your hands.

   (f) Stay behind the white line.

2. Use clear, concise language to rewrite these using command verbs.

   For example:
   It is important that when you arrive home after a long day at school that you go to your bedroom and take your schoolbag with you and put it in your room.

   Could be written as: **Take your bag to your room.**
                            or
                            Put your bag away.

   (a) When you go out for a drive with your family in the country, where you will probably be travelling at high speed, you must always remember to fasten the seatbelt that is provided for your use.

   _____

   (b) After you have poured the milk into the mixture of flour, sugar and eggs that you have put into a large mixing bowl, you will need to stir all the ingredients together.

   _____

   (c) When you are driving your car down any road, even a motorway, it is most important that you always remember to drive on the correct side of the road.

   _____

   (d) People should always remember that before they eat breakfast, lunch, dinner or even a snack, it is important that they go to the bathroom and make sure they have washed their hands with soap and water.

   _____

   (e) It is important that you collect any rubbish left after you have finished eating your lunch and that you go and put it in the bins provided for this purpose.

   _____

Choose one topic from the box and use the framework to plan and write a procedure. You may need to research appropriate information on the Internet, in the library, or seek advice from another person.

| *planting seeds* | *growing tomatoes* | *making scones* | *cooking rice* |

Title _____

Goal

_____

_____

_____

Requirements

_____

_____

_____

_____

Steps

_____

_____

_____

_____

_____

_____

_____

_____

_____

_____

_____

_____

Test (How do you know if you have been successful?)

_____

_____

_____

Use the checklist below to edit and proofread your work.

You will be self-editing for:

Spelling   Punctuation

Grammar   Concise language

You will use a peer editor to check:

Clear instructions

Sense

Checklist

Title of procedure: _____

1. Does your procedure make sense to you? .... ○ **yes** ○ **no**

2. Did you include a goal? .... ○ **yes** ○ **no**

3. Did you list the things you needed? .... ○ **yes** ○ **no**

4. Have you included all the steps in the correct order? .... ○ **yes** ○ **no**

5. Did you add a test to check that your procedure works? .... ○ **yes** ○ **no**

6. Have you corrected any spelling errors? .... ○ **yes** ○ **no**

   • Did you check that your words look right? .... ○ **yes** ○ **no**

   • Did you use a dictionary? .... ○ **yes** ○ **no**

   • Did you ask someone? .... ○ **yes** ○ **no**

7. Have you used command verbs? .... ○ **yes** ○ **no**

8. Are your statements short and clear? .... ○ **yes** ○ **no**

9. Does each sentence make sense when read on its own? .... ○ **yes** ○ **no**

10. Do all your statements have capital letters and full stops? .... ○ **yes** ○ **no**

11. Is your procedure written in the present tense? .... ○ **yes** ○ **no**

12. Ask a partner to read your procedure.

    Did she/he find it easy to understand? .... ○ **yes** ○ **no**

1. Choose a topic from the box and plan, then write, a procedure on a separate sheet of paper.

   Washing a dog   *Setting a table*
   Cleaning teeth   *Taking a photo*
   Washing a car   *Making popcorn*

2. **Text:**

   A procedure may have a _____, a list of _____,

   steps to follow and a _____ at the end.

   Language:

   A procedure uses _____, _____ statements.

3. Complete these statements:

   (a) Procedures are usually written in the _____ tense.

   (b) It is important to follow the steps in the correct order because …

4. A suffix is attached to the _____ of a word.

5. Ad **ly** to these words:

   (a) suitable _____   (b) sole _____

   (c) horrible _____   (d) feeble _____

   (e) responsible _____   (f) vile _____

6. Add **ly** to these words.

   (a) happy _____   (b) heavy _____

   (c) shy _____   (d) busy _____

   (e) greedy _____   (f) sly _____

7. Add **ed** or **ing** to these words.

   (a) picnic _____   (b) panic _____

   (c) traffic _____   (d) mimic _____

8. Complete these statements.

    (a) Adverbs of place tell _____ something is happening.

    (b) Adverbs of time tell _____ something is happening.

    (c) Adverbs of manner tell _____ something is happening.

---

9. Underline the verb. Circle the adverbs.

    (a) The girl ran inside.   (b) The boy swam slowly.

    (c) He crept silently.   (d) She arrived late.

    (e) The baby laughed happily.   (f) Brad sneezed suddenly.

    (g) She ate hungrily.   (h) We went outside.

---

10. Choose an adverb from the box to tell how, when or where these things happened.

tomorrow	*loudly*	*carefully*	*yesterday*	*outside*

    (a) Take the lid off _____ then add the pasta.

    (b) _____ I'll be watching my team play football.

    (c) Please put the cat's food _____.

    (d) The band played _____ and we couldn't sleep.

    (e) _____ I forgot my library book.

11. Write a sentence using these adverbs.

    (a) *often*

    (b) *softly*

    (c) *inside*

12. Change the adjectives to adverbs by adding suffixes.

    (a) wise   _____   (b) truthful _____

    (c) helpful   _____   (d) happy   _____

    (e) soft   _____   (f) sad   _____

Waterskiing at Point Watson

A recount is a **retelling** of **past events** in time order.

Read the recount.

Waterskiing at Point Watson

Yesterday I went waterskiing with the Petersons, our neighbours. All summer my sister, Bev, and I had watched them load up their blue and white ski-boat with skis, ropes, jackets, fuel and food every Saturday and Sunday morning and we wished that one day we too could try this exciting sport.

On Saturday morning Mr Peterson noticed us watching them and came over to the fence and asked us if we had tried to ski. We couldn't believe our luck when, after we said 'No', he invited us to meet them down at the river the very next day.

We were packed and ready to go by 7 o'clock on Sunday morning, but we had to wait for two hours before Dad drove us to Point Watson. There were three other ski-boats there, all speeding around the river in a big loop with skiers clinging to ropes behind them.

After watching for a while it was finally our turn. Bev decided that she would have the first go. Mr Peterson helped her to put on the skis and ski jacket and told her to keep her arms straight, her knees bent and to lean back and just hold on. She looked very awkward as the boat gathered speed and she wobbled along behind it before falling off. The boat went around her in a big circle and she tried again and again and again.

At last it was my turn. I felt the water rushing past me and before I knew it I was standing up … well, almost! I was so excited, then the rope went slack before pulling me forwards and I hit the water. It took me a while to realise what had happened and to let go of the rope. Mr Peterson told me not to pull on the rope but to let it pull me along and it worked. I must have skied along for three minutes before I hit a bit of a wave and off I came.

What a wonderful morning we had! I can't wait until next week, when Mr Peterson has invited us to have another try. I'm sure I'll be able to do it and then I am going to have a go at skiing on a single ski.

Partner activity

1. (a) Do you think that you would like to try to waterski?   ◯ **yes** ◯ **no**

   Try to think of at least five good reasons for your decision. You may like to write them down, starting with the most important reason.

   1. _____
   2. _____
   3. _____
   4. _____
   5. _____

   (b) With your partner, both of you explain why you would or would not like to try waterskiing.

   I would like to waterski because …
   OR
   I wouldn't like to waterski because …

   (c) After you have listened to each other's talk, both of you answer the questions.

   • Did your partner speak clearly?.. ◯ **yes** ◯ **no**

   • Did she/he look at you? (the audience) .... ◯ **yes** ◯ **no**

   • Did the explanation make sense? .... ◯ **yes** ◯ **no**

   • Were the arguments logical? .... ◯ **yes** ◯ **no**

   • Was your partner persuasive?.. ◯ **yes** ◯ **no**

Class activity

2. (a) Accidents can happen in any sport. Brainstorm possible dangers involved in waterskiing and compile a list.

   (b) Rank these, starting with the most likely danger down to the least likely.

   (c) Discuss measures that could help to minimise each danger.

   (d) What do you think is the greatest danger?_____

   _____

   (e) Explain how you would minimise it. _____

   _____

   _____

Structure

This recount has:

A title..What the recount is about

A setting..Who, where and when it happened

The events...What happened and the order of events

An ending/comment...................................The ending and what the writer thinks about it

Read the recount *Waterskiing at Point Watson* again and answer the questions.

1. **Title**

    What is the recount about? _____

2. **Setting**

    (a) Who was learning to waterski? _____

    (b) Who taught them? _____

    (c) Who took them to the river? _____

    (d) Where did they go? _____

    (e) When did they go waterskiing? _____

3. **Events**

    (a) What did the children watch every weekend? _____

    _____

    (b) What did Mr Peterson do one Saturday morning? _____

    _____

    (c) What happened at 7 o'clock on Sunday? _____

    _____

    (d) When did they go to the river? _____

    (e) What did they see when they reached Point Watson? _____

    (f) Who tried to ski first? _____

    (g) Did she ski well? ◯ **yes** ◯ **no**   (h) Did the writer have a turn? ◯ **yes** ◯ **no**

4. **Ending**

    (a) How did the writer feel? _____

    (b) What is going to happen next weekend? _____

Reading for information

1.   True or false? Colour the correct answer.

(a)   The two children went waterskiing with the Petersons on Saturday.   ○ **true** ○ **false**

(b)   The Petersons went skiing regularly.   ○ **true** ○ **false**

(c)   You should try to keep your legs straight when learning to waterski.   ○ **true** ○ **false**

(d)   Bev fell off the skis many times.   ○ **true** ○ **false**

(e)   There were four ski-boats at Point Watson.   ○ **true** ○ **false**

Reading for understanding

1.   (a) Do you think Mr Peterson is a kind man?

○ **yes** ○ **no**

Why do you think he invited the children to go waterskiing with them?

(b)   Bev had first try at skiing. Did she do well? ○ **yes** ○ **no**

How do you think the writer felt about it?

(c)   Why do you think the children were ready to go skiing so early?

_____

_____

(d)   Do you think the writer is a confident person? ○ **yes** ○ **no**

Explain why you think this. _____

_____

_____

Applying your knowledge

Safety is a very important consideration in all sport, but because of speed, water, fuel and the boat's propeller, waterskiing can be dangerous.

Read these rules and add some of your own to the list. You may like to work with a partner.

Waterskiing rules

- The boat driver must be more than 18 years of age. _____
- There must be an observer in the boat. _____
- _____
- _____
- _____
- _____

Vocabulary

Synonyms are words with the same or similar meanings.

For example: **big** and **large**

wealthy and **rich**

1. Write a synonym for these words from the recount, *Waterskiing at Point Watson*.

   (a) tried _____   (b) hold _____

   (c) helped _____   (d) keep _____

   (e) watching _____   (f) clinging _____

   (g) luck _____   (h) finally _____

2. Change the bold word in each sentence to a synonym. The meaning should remain the same.

   (a) The boat took off with a **thundering** roar. _____

   (b) The skier dropped the rope and glided in towards the **shore**. _____

   (c) The family had a **great** day at the river. _____

   (d) I think waterskiing is a **good** family sport. _____

3. (a) Read this passage. Underline all the **nice** words.

> The river is very nice. I enjoy
> going there on a nice day. There
> is a nice little beach with nice
> white sand and some nice trees.
> I often run down there. I play in
> the nice sand before I dive into
> the nice cool water.

(b) Use synonyms for the word **nice** and rewrite the passage.

Try to choose interesting, descriptive synonyms to make your passage more interesting and appealing.

The river

_____

_____

_____

_____

_____

_____

_____

_____

_____

_____

_____

_____

_____

_____

_____

_____

Jumbled words

4.   Unjumble these words from the text.

   (a) virre _____   (b) ckajte _____   (c) tsopr _____

Spelling

Changing short vowels to long vowels

> **Spelling rule**
>
> The letter **e** at the end of a word changes a short vowel sound to a long vowel sound.
>
> > Read these words and notice how this rule works.
> >
> > mat – mate   pet – Pete
> >
> > hid – hide   rod – rode
> >
> > cub – cube

1.   Add **e** to these short vowel words to make words with long vowel sound. Then use the words with long vowel sounds in sentences.

   (a)   plan

   (b)   slid

   (c)   slop

   (d)   plum

Double consonants

Some words need the final consonant to be doubled before adding a suffix. (A suffix is a group of letters added to the end of a word. For example: **ing**, **y**, **ed**.)

   ho**p**   ho**pp**ing   su**n**   su**nn**y   sli**p**   sli**pp**ed

Other words don't. For example:

   mil**k**   mil**k**ing   jum**p**   jum**p**ing   stan**d** stan**d**ing

There is a spelling rule to help with this.

> ### Spelling rule
>
> When adding a suffix to a word, **two** consonants keep the vowel short.

1. (a) Are all the first vowels short in the words with suffixes above?   ◯ **yes** ◯ **no**

    (b) Do they all have two consonants after the first vowel?   ◯ **yes** ◯ **no**

2. Read these words with short vowel sounds, then write the word with a suffix added. Follow the rule to keep the vowel short.

    (a) bump _____   (b) run _____

    (c) shop _____   (d) hand _____

> These words have **long** vowel sounds.
>
>   mating   hoping   sloping
>
> These words have **short** vowel sounds.
>
>   matting   hopping   slopping

3. Circle the correct word to complete each sentence. Remember, two consonants keep the vowel short.

    (a) I was *hoping/hopping* you could come to the beach.

    (b) The boy was *sloping/slopping* the milk over the floor.

    (c) The floor was covered with grass *mating/matting*.

    (d) She *hoped/hopped* to the door.

    (e) The hill *slopped/sloped* gradually down to the river.

    (f) The frog was *hoping/hopping* around the edge of the pond.

    (g) Some birds do a *matting/mating* dance in spring.

Collective nouns

Collective nouns are the names used for groups. For example: a **flock** of sheep.

1. Choose a collective noun from the box and write it on the line.

| class | herd | forest | swarm |

(a) A _____ of trees.   (b) A _____ of pupils.

(c) A _____ of cattle.   (d) A _____ of bees.

2. Use the words from the box to complete the story.

| album | pack | bunch | flock | team |

The football _____ was sitting waiting for the coach to arrive.

One boy had a _____ of cards and wanted people to play cards.

Another boy was keen to show the others his stamp _____.

Some boys were hungry and persuaded John to share his _____

of grapes.

Others just sat quietly watching a _____ of birds on the oval.

3. Write the word from the box to name these groups.

| fruit | occupations | meat | vegetables | countries |

(a) steak, chops, lamb, sausage _____

(b) orange, banana, apple, pear _____

(c) India, China, Indonesia, Canada _____

(d) doctor, dentist, plumber, painter _____

(e) onion, potato, carrot, peas _____

4. There are some quite unusual collective nouns that we don't often hear; for example, a **murder** of crows.

(a) Research other unusual collective nouns and compile a class list. You may like to have a competition to see who finds the most interesting or unusual **collective noun**.

(b) Which two collective nouns do you think are the most interesting?

(i) a _____ of _____   (ii) a _____ of _____

Pronouns

Pronouns are used to take the place of **nouns**. For example; **he, they, I, his.**

If we didn't have **pronouns**, we would have to write:

> On Saturday morning Ben said that **Ben** wanted to go to the river. Mum said that **Mum** would take **Ben** but **Mum** couldn't stay long because **Mum** had to have **Mum's** hair cut.

1. (a) Rewrite the story using **pronouns** to replace the bold nouns.

    _____

    _____

    _____

    _____

    _____

    (b) Which pronoun did you use most? _____

Personal pronouns

Personal pronouns identify three different categories of people.

The **first person** is the person speaking; for example, I, me, mine, we, us.

The **second person** is the person spoken to; for example, you, yours.

The **third person** is the person spoken about; for example, he, her, they, them.

2. Unjumble these sentences using your knowledge of pronouns. Remember to start with a capital letter and end with a full stop.

    (a) stopped he the car

    _____

    (b) from I bus helped him the

    _____

    (c) went dance to they the

    _____

    (d) forgot bring he books the to

    _____

    (e) bags belong the us to

    _____

3. Change the bold words from the first person to the third person. The first one has been done. Remember, the third person is the person spoken about.

   (a) **I** enjoy riding **my** bike fast.

   He enjoys riding his bike fast.

   (b) **I** have looked everywhere for **my** dog.

   _____

   (c) **We** were pleased that **our** team won.

   _____

   (d) Where did **I** leave **my** bags?

   _____

   (e) Why are **we** still waiting for **our** bus?

   _____

4. Underline the pronoun in each sentence.

   (a) I like to go fishing with my dad.   (b) They enjoyed taking the boat out on the river.

   (c) We learnt to waterski with friends.   (d) Bev enjoys waterskiing because it is fun.

   (e) Where did Tom put it?   (f) Our teacher put her keys down and can't find them.

5. Use a pronoun from the box to complete each sentence.

it	*they*	*she*	*them*	*he*	*we*	*I*	*you*

   (a) My grandfather is old and _____ can't walk very fast.

   (b) I wonder where _____ are going for their Christmas holidays.

   (c) When _____ go for a swim, don't forget to take your bathers and a towel.

   (d) Bree was sad because _____ couldn't find her netball.

   (e) You'll need to help me put this in the top cupboard because _____ am too short to reach it.

   (f) When do you think the bus will be here? I seem to have been waiting for

   _____ for hours.

   (g) These swim fins are really great and I'm so pleased my brother gave _____ to me when he got his new ones.

   (h) _____ will be going to London for our family reunion in April.

Sequencing

Writing the events of a recount in the order in which they happen is important.

1. Read the recount *Going to bed* then list five of the events in the correct order.

> **Going to bed**
>
> I usually go to bed about eight o'clock. After I have said goodnight to my parents, I go to the toilet, have a shower and put on my pyjamas. Before I climb into bed, I clean my teeth and pour myself a glass of water. I am allowed to read for about 15 minutes before I turn off the light and go to sleep.

Events:

* _____
* _____
* _____
* _____
* _____

2. Number these events in the correct sequence.

Have breakfast .... ☐

Get out of bed .... ☐

Go to school .... ☐

Clean teeth .... ☐

Have lunch .... ☐

Start schoolwork .... ☐

3. Think about the things you do and the order in which you do them.

List at least five events involved in cleaning your teeth.

* _____
* _____
* _____
* _____
* _____

Use the plan below to write a recount about a visit you had to one of the following:

| *beach* | *river* | *lake* | *waterslide* | *swimming pool* |

Title _____

Setting

Who _____

Where _____

When _____

Why _____

Events

1. _____

_____

_____

_____

2. _____

_____

_____

_____

3. _____

_____

_____

_____

4. _____

_____

_____

_____

Concluding statement/Comment

_____

_____

After you have written your recount in full, edit and proofread your work using the checklist below.

You will be self-editing for:

Spelling   Punctuation

Grammar   Sentence structure

You will use a peer editor to check:

Sense

Sequence

Checklist

Title of recount: _____

1. Does your recount include:

    (a)   specific characters? .... ⭘ **yes** ⭘ **no**

    (b)   location or setting? .... ⭘ **yes** ⭘ **no**

    (c)   time when the events took place? .... ⭘ **yes** ⭘ **no**

    (d)   why these events occurred? .... ⭘ **yes** ⭘ **no**

2. Were your events listed in correct order? .... ⭘ **yes** ⭘ **no**

3. Did your recount finish with a concluding comment or statement? .... ⭘ **yes** ⭘ **no**

4. (a)   Have you corrected any spelling errors? .... ⭘ **yes** ⭘ **no**

    (b)   Have you used capital letters and full stops? .... ⭘ **yes** ⭘ **no**

    (c)   Did you include action verbs? .... ⭘ **yes** ⭘ **no**

    (d)   Did you use conjunctions? .... ⭘ **yes** ⭘ **no**

    (e)   Did you use the past tense? .... ⭘ **yes** ⭘ **no**

Ask a partner to read your recount.

5. (a)   Was your partner able to follow the sequence? .... ⭘ **yes** ⭘ **no**

    (b)   Did it make sense? .... ⭘ **yes** ⭘ **no**

1. Choose a title from the box and plan, then write, a recount on a separate sheet of paper.

   The first time I tried to ...   *My wish came true*

   The wait was worth it   *I always wanted to ...*

2. Complete the following.

   Text

   A recount is

   Structure

   A recount has:

   - A _____
   - Setting _____
   - _____
   - _____

3. Answer the questions.

   (a) The **setting** discusses _____

   _____ and

   _____ the events happen.

   (b) The **events** tell _____

   happens and are told in correct

   _____.

   (c) The **comment** is a concluding statement which tells _____

   _____

   _____

4. Synonyms are words with the _____ meaning.

5. Match the synonyms.

   (a) house •   • ill   (f) intersection •   • ship

   (b) disappear •   • home   (g) swift •   • talkative

   (c) touch •   • vanish   (h) boat •   • crossing

   (d) sick •   • scare   (i) naughty •   • rapid

   (e) fright •   • feel   (j) chatty •   • misbehaved

6. Read the passage from the fairy tale *Jack and the beanstalk* and change the bold words for a synonym.

Once upon a time there was a boy called Jack. He wasn't very **clever**

_____ but he didn't mind.

Jack and his **sad** _____ mother lived in a **tiny**

_____ **cottage** _____ with a cat and an **old**

_____ cow **called** _____ Daisy. Jack and his

mother were **very** _____ poor. When there was no money left, Jack

had to take Daisy to the market to sell. Jack's mother **pushed** _____

him out of the door and told him to **come back** _____ immediately.

Jack nodded and set off **down** _____ the road.

7. When adding a suffix to a word, two consonants keep the vowel _____ .

8. Circle the correct word to complete each sentence.

(a) The boy rode his bike down the sloping/slopping hill.

(b) I was hoping/hopping you could read this story to me.

(c) The workmen covered the floor with new matting/mating.

Collective nouns are the names used for groups of things.

9. Complete the following.

(a) a _____ of sheep   (b) a _____ of elephants

(c) a _____ of pupils   (d) a _____ of bees

(e) a _____ of trees   (f) a _____ of birds

(g) a _____ of geese   (h) a _____ of flowers

(i) an _____ of stamps   (j) a _____ of wolves

10. Pronouns are used to take the place of _____ .

11. Read the extract from *The elves and the shoemaker*. Change the bold nouns to pronouns.

SNIP, SNIP. TAP! TAP! STITCH, STITCH. The shoemaker's shop was very small but

very busy. All day long the shoemaker snipped, stitched and tapped. **The shoemaker**

_____ made slippers, boots and shoes. The shoemaker's wife swept

and tidied. **The shoemaker's wife** _____ sang as she worked. As the

months and years went by, **the shoemaker and his wife** _____ grew

older and poorer. The shoemaker and his wife's shop was small and the people in the

town forgot the shop was there. **The people in the town** _____ went

to buy their shoes in the next town over the hill.

'Should we move to the new town?' asked the shoemaker's wife.

'No, this is our home', **the shoemaker** _____ replied.

12. Use a pronoun from the box to complete each sentence.

I	*it*	*her*	*you*	*they*	*we*

(a) If _____ eat all your vegetables you can have some chocolate cake.

(b) Where did your sister buy those jeans? They really look good on _____ .

(c) I wonder if _____ will be taking their boat out this weekend.

(d) _____ want you to tidy up your room before you go to the beach.

(e) My grandparents' car is new and _____ looks very sporty.

(f) Our team trains hard because _____ have a good chance of winning the final.

13. Underline the pronoun in each sentence.

(a) Where did you leave your bike?

(b) I left my bike at school.

(c) Then we will have to go back there as soon as possible.

Burger Bar

Expositions are written to **persuade others to think** or **do something**.

Read this exposition advertising Burger Bars.

Burger Bars

You want one now
You need one now
You gotta have one NOW!

It's the new Burger Bar – all the taste, all the flavour of a juicy grilled beef burger, with tomato, lettuce, pickles and crispy fries, transformed into a chewy pocket-sized bar you can take anywhere.

Then, no matter where you are when the munchies hit, you're ready. Just peel back the foil wrapper and sink your teeth into the freshest, tastiest meal you can hold in one hand.

Life's too short to waste time waiting to eat.

New Burger Bar – ready when you are!
Tell Mum to get one NOW!

Available at good supermarkets everywhere!

Class activity

1. Discuss what you already know about burgers to complete the flow chart below.

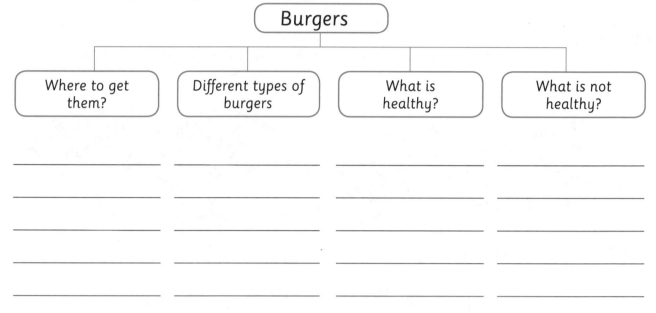

Partner activity

2. Discuss why burgers are so popular with children and young adults.

3. Compile a list of good things about burgers.

4. Write a short (10 words or fewer) slogan to try to sell a particular burger. Include some of the ideas you and your partner discussed.

    Remember that you need to try to persuade people that these burgers are the best and that they should buy lots of them.

Structure

An exposition can promote and sell by using persuasive language. This exposition has:

A title: Tells what the exposition is about.

An overview: Briefly tells what the writer thinks about the subject.

Reasons: Arguments to persuade people.

Conclusion: Final comment and summing up.

1.   Read the advertisement for Burger Bars again.

Answer these questions.

Title
What is the advertisement trying to sell? _____

Overview
What does the writer want people to do? _____
_____

Reasons

(i)   What do the Burger Bars taste like? _____
_____

(ii)   How are they wrapped? _____
_____

(iii)   Why do they save you time? _____
_____

(iv)   Where can you buy them? _____
_____

(v)   Why are they so easy to eat? _____
_____

(vi)   Why are they so easy to carry? _____
_____

Conclusion
Why should people buy these Burger Bars? _____
_____

Reading for information

1. True or false? Colour the correct answer.

   (a) You can see fresh, real tomatoes and lettuce in Burger Bars.   ◯ **true** ◯ **false**

   (b) You can taste grilled beef in these Burger Bars.   ◯ **true** ◯ **false**

   (c) Burger Bars are wrapped in paper and are served in a box.   ◯ **true** ◯ **false**

   (d) Burger Bars are new.   ◯ **true** ◯ **false**

   (e) You don't have to wait for Burger Bars to be made at a shop.   ◯ **true** ◯ **false**

Reading for understanding

1. (a) Does the advertisement tell you how much Burger Bars cost? ◯ **yes** ◯ **no**

   Why? _____

   _____

   _____

   (b) Would you like to try one of these Burger Bars? ◯ **yes** ◯ **no**

   Explain your reasons. _____

   _____

   _____

   (c) Why does the advertisement want you to tell Mum to buy you one instead of suggesting you should buy one yourself?

   _____

   _____

   (d) Do you think this is a good advertisement? ◯ **yes** ◯ **no**

   Give two reasons.

Applying your knowledge

Make a poster to advertise a new ice-cream product.

You will need to decide:

- What your product is.
- What it is made of.
- What it looks like.
- What it tastes like.
- How it is served.
- What is special about it.
- Why people would want to try it.

- How much it costs.
- Where you can buy it.
- How big it is.
- What shape it is.
- Who your customers are.
- Why it is good for you.
- What it is called.

Think about making your poster:

- attractive
- eye-catching
- informative
- colourful
- easy to read

Remember, your task is to persuade other people that they really should buy this product.

1. Find words about burgers to complete this acrostic poem.

B _____

U _____

R _____

G _____

E _____

R _____

B _____

A _____

R _____

S _____

2. What are some of the ingredients you would like to have in a real burger?

_____

_____

3. Word diamond.

Use the clues to complete this puzzle.

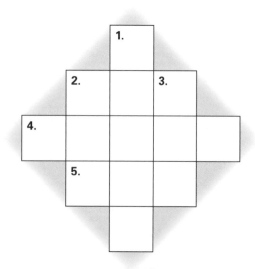

Across   2. Burgers _____ good for you.

4. Chocolates are a special _____.

5. There is black _____ on the road.

Down   1. I like to eat _____ and butter.

2. She enjoys _____ lessons.

3. She is deaf in one _____.

Alliteration

Advertisements often use **alliteration** to attract attention.

For example:

Beefy **B**urger **B**ars

Cool **c**areless **c**ats

Alliteration is the use of the same sound at the beginning of words.

4. Create your own alliteration by adding words beginning with the same consonants.

(a) _____ snakes   (b) _____ hairdressers

(c) _____ babies   (d) _____ students

(e) _____ dentists   (f) _____ dancers

(g) _____ tigers   (h) _____ bees

5.

(a) How many words using alliteration are in this advertisement? _____

Challenge

(b) Illustrate and write your own advertisement for a product you like, using more alliteration than the Melting Moments advertisement.

(c) How many words with alliteration did you use?

_____

(d) What was the class record?

_____

1. Word puzzle

    Use the clues to find words with the letters **bo** in them.

    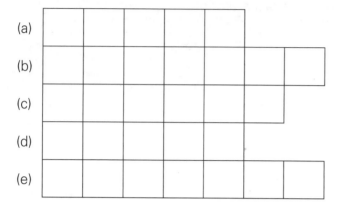

    (a)

    (b)

    (c)

    (d)

    (e)

    (a) The joint in the middle of your arm

    (b) A beautiful arc in the sky

    (c) No-one

    (d) To say how good you are

    (e) A very young baby

An or A

Burger Bars is an exposition.

Note that we say **an** exposition, not **a** exposition.

The word **exposition** starts with a vowel and saying two vowel sounds is difficult so a consonant is added (an).

1. Try saying the words in the box below with **a** or **an**.

elephant	ant	idiot	eagle
uncle	orange	egg	angel

2. Which was easier?_____

3. Write **a** or **an** in front of these words. Say each one to hear which sounds better.

    (a) _____ ambulance

    (b) _____ tree

    (c) _____ hospital

    (d) _____ branch

    (e) _____ accident

    (f) _____ apple

Two vowels

Two vowels together can make just one sound.

For example:

ai	**rain**	ie	**pie**	ea	**leaf**	ui	**fruit**
ue	**glue**	oe	**toe**	oa	**boat**	eo	**people**

There is a rhyme that is often used to help people to remember this.

> When two little vowels go walking
> The first one does the talking
> and says its name.

Try these: ai   ee   ue   oe   eo   ie

Of course this rule doesn't always work. For example: **ou** does not make an **o** sound.

But it is still a useful rule to remember.

4. Complete the double vowel word in each sentence.

(a) She will gl_____ _____ the pictures in the book.

(b) He can s_____ _____l a boat.

(c) His new shirt is bl_____ _____.

(d) The sh_____ _____p were in the paddock.

(e) There were lots of p_____ _____ple at the show.

(f) I hope that canoe will fl_____ _____t.

(g) The bee stung the boy on his t_____ _____.

LANGUAGE FEATURES

Capital letters

Capital letters are needed at the beginning of sentences. They are also used for the names of people, places, products, days, months, books and films.

For example:

Little Red Riding Hood, Mrs Jones, Doctor Hu, Madonna, September, Monday, Potomac River, The Tower of London, Paris, Mars Bars™, Chrysler, *Finding Nemo*.

These are all called **proper nouns**.

Nouns are naming words, but when they name particular people, places and things like those listed above, they are called **proper nouns** and always need a capital letter.

1. Find proper nouns for each category.

Category	Proper nouns
people	
places	
products	
days	
months	

2. Punctuate by adding capital letters to start sentences and for proper nouns.

    (a) skateboards are popular in san franscisco, particularly on saturday and sunday.

    (b) the children from margaret river primary school went on an excursion to visit the museum of childhood in perth.

    (c) my mother took me to see doctor walsh after I twisted my ankle playing hockey last friday.

    (d) the combined choir from trinity college and presbyterian ladies college is singing in london and in wales in july.

3. Complete these sentences using proper nouns.

    (a) My best friend is _____ .

    (b) The best day of the week is _____ .

    (c) Our family car is a _____ .

    (d) My favourite chocolate is _____ .

    (e) The band I like best is _____ .

    (f) I like to watch _____ on TV.

    (g) A team I support is _____ .

4. The passage below needs 8 capital letters, 4 full stops and 2 question marks.

    are you concerned about recycling i am i think that it is disgusting that fast food restaurants like monster burgers produce so much disposable waste everything is wrapped in paper or cardboard and people just throw it all away can't they be made more aware of environmental issues the government should introduce and enforce regulations to ensure that unnecessary packaging is reduced

Introductory statements

The introductory statement briefly tells what the author thinks about the subject. It states his/her point of view.

1. Read these paragraphs. What is the author's position? The first one has been done.

(a)
> On 26 January each year, Australians celebrate Australia Day. It is a national holiday. Some people enjoy this day and celebrations and fireworks take place around the country. Other people find it difficult to get involved. It is an important date and everyone should participate.

The author believes __Australia Day is important.__

(b)
> The summer months are very long and dry. Many people enjoy picnics and camping during this time and should observe the rules about lighting campfires and barbecues.

The author believes _____

_____

_____

(c)
> We sometimes think that people can't make a difference. But they can. When it comes to the River Thames, we all have a job to do. We must look after it so that our children and grandchildren can enjoy it. It is important to pick up our rubbish, especially plastic bags.

The author believes _____

_____

_____

(d)
> There are many children today who have difficulty with reading and spelling. Schools should be doing more about this problem by making sure that children have homework they must do instead of wasting time watching TV and playing on computers every night.

The author believes _____

_____

_____

Preparing an exposition

2. (a) Write your ideas in the spaces provided on this exposition plan.

Title	Takeaway food
Overview	I believe _____ _____ _____
Arguments	1. _____ _____ _____ 2. _____ _____ _____ 3. _____ _____ _____ 4. _____ _____ _____
Conclusion	_____ _____

(b) Your arguments need to be strong to persuade others to think or do as you want. Good writers use their strongest arguments first.

Which of your four arguments do you consider to be the most persuasive?

Why? _____

_____

Persuasive arguments

3. Write two strong arguments for or against these statements.

(a) **Soft drink is good for you.**

1. _____   **2.** _____

_____   _____

_____   _____

_____   _____

(b) **School uniforms should be compulsory.**

1. _____   **2.** _____

_____   _____

_____   _____

_____   _____

(c) **Computers are educational.**

1. _____   **2.** _____

_____   _____

_____   _____

_____   _____

4. Highlight your stronger argument in each of the above examples.

Getting the message across

5. Messages should be **clear** and **persuasive**. Write **C** (clear), **P** (persuasive) or **CP** (both) next to the following messages.

Choose one of the three topics from *Persuasive arguments* on page 131. Use the plan to help you organise your ideas then, write your exposition in full on a separate sheet of paper.

Title

Introductory statement

(What do you believe?) _____

_____

_____

Arguments

(Thoughts and ideas which support what you believe.) _____

_____

_____

_____

_____

_____

_____

_____

_____

_____

_____

_____

_____

_____

_____

Conclusion

(Link your ideas together to form a final comment which summarises your position.)

_____

_____

_____

After you have written your exposition in full, use this checklist to edit and proofread your work.

You will self-editing for:

Spelling   Punctuation

Grammar   Sentence structure

You will be using a peer editor to check:

Sense

Persuasion

Checklist

Title of exposition: _____

1. Do you understand the purpose of an exposition? .... ◯ **yes** ◯ **no**

2. Does your exposition:

   (a) clearly state a problem in the introduction? .... ◯ **yes** ◯ **no**

   (b) provide background information? .... ◯ **yes** ◯ **no**

   (c) list facts to support arguments?
       (diagrams, photographs, facts and figures) .... ◯ **yes** ◯ **no**

   (d) sequence arguments from strongest to weakest? .... ◯ **yes** ◯ **no**

   (e) include a final paragraph which reinforces and summarises
       the main points? .... ◯ **yes** ◯ **no**

3. Have you used persuasive words? .... ◯ **yes** ◯ **no**

4. Ask a partner to read your exposition.

   (a) Did he or she understand your point of view? .... ◯ **yes** ◯ **no**

   (b) Did it make sense? .... ◯ **yes** ◯ **no**

   (c) Were you able to persuade your partner to agree with
       your point of view? .... ◯ **yes** ◯ **no**

1. Choose a topic from the box and plan, then write, an exposition in full on a separate sheet of paper. The exposition may be in the form of an essay, an advertisement or a letter. Use a framework to plan your exposition.

> *Junk food*   *TV advertising during children's shows*
>   *Fruit and vegetables*

2. Complete the following.

    (a) Expositions are written to _____

    _____

    (b) Expositions use _____ language.

3. Write **a** or **an** in front of these words.

    (a) _____ bird   (b) _____ ant   (c) _____ eagle

    (d) _____ elephant   (e) _____ monkey   (f) _____ cow

4. Complete the double vowel word in each sentence.

    (a) The bus tr_____ _____d to overtake the car.

    (b) The dentist put fluoride on his t_____ _____th.

    (c) The sky is bl_____ _____.

    (d) May I pl_____ _____se have an ice-cream?

    (e) I love to eat fresh fr_____ _____t.

    (f) The l_____ _____f fell from the tree.

5. Punctuate each sentence by adding full stops and using a coloured pencil or pen to add the missing capital letters.

    (a) my teacher drove her new car from limerick to tralee

    (b) please come to my party on wednesday

    (c) during the summer holidays, david and harry enjoyed

      swimming in dunmore east

    (d) doctor green works at wesley hospital near queen's park

    (e) we had pizza for dinner last friday

6. Rewrite the sentences below using full stops and capital letters.

> my favourite food is fish every saturday night my parents take us to joe's, our local fish and chip shop and they buy dinner for monica and me we really love saturday i would love to have fish and chips for dinner every night of the week

_____

_____

_____

_____

_____

_____

7. Complete these sentences using proper nouns.

(a) My mother's name is

(b) My favourite book is

(c) My birthday is in

(d) I live in

(e) My street is

(f) My father's name is

(g) My teacher's name is

8. Create your own alliteration by adding words to describe each noun.

(a) _____ caterpillars

(b) _____ balloons

(c) _____ computers

(d) _____ shirts

(e) _____ dogs

True justice

A narrative describes a **series of events** and **circumstances** often involving fictitious characters.

Read the narrative.

True justice

It was a really hot day, so hot that the air burnt Peter's skin and it even seemed hard to breathe. Any movement he made was an effort and everyone was irritable and bad-tempered. The Wilson family decided to take their boat out on the river to escape the intense heat.

When they arrived at the boat launching ramp, it seemed that everyone in the city who owned a boat must have had the same idea. There were people, boats, trailers and vehicles everywhere. The people looked hot and bothered, all just wanting to get their boats into the water and be off, but they were waiting their turn in two long queues.

Suddenly, there was a screech of tyres and an expensive four-wheel drive arrived, towing a shiny new boat. It backed straight down the middle of the ramp, pushing in and blocking off all the others. After two men had unhitched the boat, the driver, a fat, red-faced man, sped off to park his car and trailer. The people waiting just couldn't believe their eyes. They were all too amazed to say or do anything.

The driver strode down the ramp, ignoring all the stunned, silent people and climbed into his boat. The motor roared and they set off ... but something didn't look right. It soon became obvious to the spectators that the beautiful new boat was sitting very low in the water and that it was, in fact, sinking very fast!

In their haste to get going, the inexperienced sailors had forgotten to replace the plugs in the back of their boat. Water was pouring into the boat and they were rapidly going down.

The spectators suddenly came to life, clapping their hands, cheering and yelling with delight as they watched the men's frantic efforts to save their boat.

Class activity

Do you prefer hot or cold weather?

Brainstorm the advantages and disadvantages of hot weather. For example, think about how you feel, the things you can and can't do, the clothing you need, the dangers and delights.

Partner activity

1. Compile a list of:

(a)
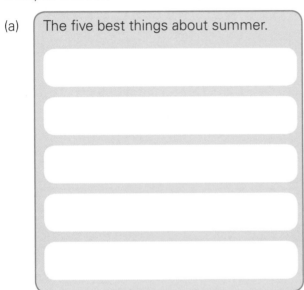
The five best things about summer.

(b)

The five best things about winter.

2. You have one minute to explain to your partner why:

   I like summer better than winter.   OR   **I like winter better than summer.**

Structure of a narrative

Structure

This narrative has:

A title	• Indicates what the story is about
	• Gets the reader's attention
Orientation	• *Who* Main characters and possibly minor characters are introduced
	• *What* Initiating event that starts the story
	• *Where* The setting or location
	• *When* Time the story takes place
Complication	• The problem involving the main character
Resolution	• How the problem is solved

Read the narrative *True justice* again and answer the questions.

Title

Is *True justice* a suitable title for this story? ◯ **yes** ◯ **no**

Why do you think this? _____

_____

Orientation

Who is the main character? _____

Who went to the river with him? _____

How many people were with the brand new boat? _____

What was everyone trying to do? _____

Where did this story take place? _____

When did it happen? _____

Complication

What did the men with the new boat do to upset everyone? _____

_____

Resolution

What happened to the new boat? _____

Why did this happen? _____

_____

Reading for information

1. True or false? Colour the correct answer.

    (a) Peter and his family were taking their boat out fishing in the ocean. ◯ **true** ◯ **false**

    (b) The people waiting were feeling hot and bothered. ◯ **true** ◯ **false**

    (c) There were two queues of boats waiting. ◯ **true** ◯ **false**

    (d) The people all yelled and shouted when the men with the new boat pushed in. ◯ **true** ◯ **false**

    (e) The boat was sinking because the men took off too fast. ◯ **true** ◯ **false**

Reading for understanding

1. What kind of people do you think the men with the new boat were? _____

   Why do you think this? _____

   _____

   _____

2. Do you think the people waiting should have cheered when the ⃝ **yes** ⃝ **no**
   new boat started to sink?

   Why?/Why not? _____

   _____

   _____

3. Why do you think the men didn't put the plugs into their boat? _____

   _____

   _____

4. If you were there, would you have helped the men? ⃝ **yes** ⃝ **no**

   Why?/Why not? _____

   _____

   _____

Applying your knowledge

1. We often have to wait in queues.

   Make a list of the places you have waited in
   a queue or have seen other people waiting
   for their turn.

2. What could happen if people didn't wait
   their turn and just pushed in?

   _____

   _____

   _____

   _____

   _____

   _____

   _____

3. Why do you think people push into queues?

_____

_____

_____

4. In some places, instead of waiting in a queue people are given a number and have to wait until their number is called out or it is displayed on a board.

   (a) Why do you think places like banks and supermarkets do this?

   _____

   _____

   _____

   (b) Do you think giving out numbers is a good idea? _____
       Explain why you think this.

   _____

   _____

   _____

People who push in are bullies.

5. Is this statement true or false? ○ **true** ○ **false**

   Give two reasons why you think this.

Opposites

1. Find a word in the narrative that means the opposite of:

    (a) cold _____

    (b) short _____

    (c) old _____

    (d) up _____

    (e) noisy _____

    (f) high _____

    (g) floating _____

    (h) remembered _____

Words with **opposite** meanings are called **antonyms**.

2. Join these antonyms.

    (a) long •   • cheap

    (b) pulling •   • poor

    (c) hard •   • easy

    (d) quick •   • short

    (e) expensive •   • noisy

    (f) difficult •   • soft

    (g) quiet •   • slow

    (h) wealthy •   • pushing

Synonyms

Words with **similar** meanings are called **synonyms**.

3. Join these synonyms.

    (a) fast •   • pulling

    (b) expensive •   • difficult

    (c) towing •   • lengthy

    (d) hard •   • quick

    (e) long •   • undo

    (f) unhitch •   • costly

    (g) amazed •   • quiet

    (h) silent •   • surprised

Antonyms

Adding **un**, **dis** or **in** to a word can change its meaning.
The new word is an **antonym**. It has the opposite meaning.
For example:

happy	**un**happy
appear	**dis**appear
experienced	**in**experienced

4. Add **un** to make **antonyms** of these words.

   (a) block _____

   (b) bothered _____

   (c) believable _____

   (d) do _____

   (e) hitch _____

   (f) clear _____

5. Add **dis** to make **antonyms** of these words.

   (a) like _____

   (b) honest _____

   (c) connect _____

   (d) agree _____

   (e) comfort _____

   (f) please _____

6. Add **in** to make **antonyms** of these words.

   (a) correct _____

   (b) formal _____

   (c) visible _____

   (d) complete _____

   (e) expensive _____

   (f) justice _____

7. Write a sentence with the opposite meaning by changing the highlighted words into antonyms.
    The first one has been done.

   (a) The girl wore an **expensive** dress to the party.

   The girl wore an inexpensive dress to the party.

   (b) I'm sure he is a very **dishonest** man.

   _____

   (c) She told us a **believable** story.

   _____

   (d) My coach was very **pleased** with the way our team played.

   _____

   (e) 'Your homework is **complete**', the teacher commented.

   _____

Word puzzle

8. (a) Read the clues to find words beginning with the letter **a** to complete this puzzle.

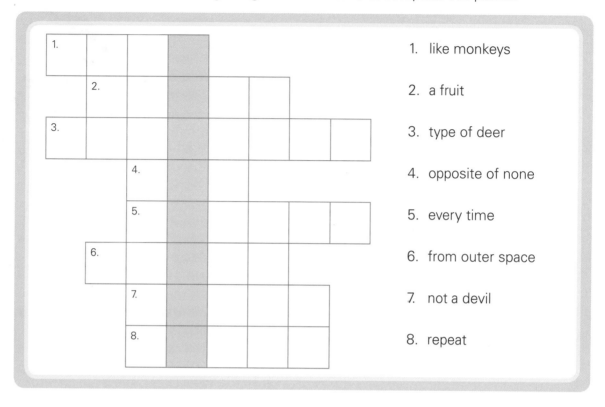

1. like monkeys

2. a fruit

3. type of deer

4. opposite of none

5. every time

6. from outer space

7. not a devil

8. repeat

(b) The letters in the shaded boxes form an important word for writers.

It is:

9. (a) Make up the clues for this **e** puzzle.

1. e	n	t	r	y

2. e	l	e	p	h	a	n	t

3. e	v	e	n

4. e	a	r	l	y

5. e	l	e	c	t	r	i	c	i	t	y

6. e	r	r	o	r

7. e	n	e	m	y

1. _____

2. _____

3. _____

4. _____

5. _____

6. _____

7. _____

(b) The letters in the shaded box form a word associated with actors.

It is:

Word maths

1. Use these word maths to spell a word from the narrative. You will need to unjumble the letters. For example: 3e + prdt = tempered.

(a) 2i + 2r + lebat = _ir_____

(b) 3e + svipnx = _ex_____

(c) 2t + 2o + fgner = _fo_____

(d) 4e + 2i + 2n + prdcx = _in_____

(e) 2o + bisvu = _ob_____

(f) 3e + vroyn = _ev_____

(g) 2h + nuietcd = _un_____

(h) 2i + 2g + 2n + or = _ig_____

2. Write an alphabetical list of words on a nautical theme. Hint: Use a dictionary to find the words and spell them correctly. For example: **a** – aquatic; **b** – beaches, **c** – coastline.

a	_____	n	_____
b	_____	o	_____
c	_____	p	_____
d	_____	q	_____
e	_____	r	_____
f	_____	s	_____
g	_____	t	_____
h	_____	u	_____
i	_____	v	_____
j	_____	w	_____
k	_____	x	_____
l	_____	y	_____
m	_____	z	_____

Syllables

A syllable is a unit of sound. Words are made up of syllables, sometimes one, sometimes more. Breaking a word into syllables (syllabification) can be a useful spelling strategy. Each syllable has only one vowel sound.

3. Find ten words from the narrative which have only one syllable; for example, hard.

_____   _____

_____   _____

_____   _____

_____   _____

_____   _____

4. Syllabify these words from the story; for example, mid/dle.

(a) trailer _____   (b) clapping _____

(c) pushing _____   (d) didn't _____

(e) anything _____   (f) replace _____

(g) intense _____   (h) looked _____

(i) waiting _____   (j) seemed _____

5. Circle the words below which have more than two syllables.

everyone	*spectators*	*escape*	*rapidly*
decided	*believe*	*launching*	*expensive*
bothered	*obvious*	*irritable*	*ignoring*

6. Add another syllable to these words.
   *Remember the rule: **e** goes away when **ing** comes to stay; for example, lik**e** – lik**ing**.*

(a) experience _____   (b) bother _____

(c) sudden _____   (d) amaze _____

(e) delight _____   (f) rapid _____

(g) expensive _____   (h) motor _____

(i) hitch _____   (j) place _____

(k) boat _____   (l) drive _____

(m) replace _____   (n) believe _____

Adjectives

1. Write five positive and five negative adjectives to describe:

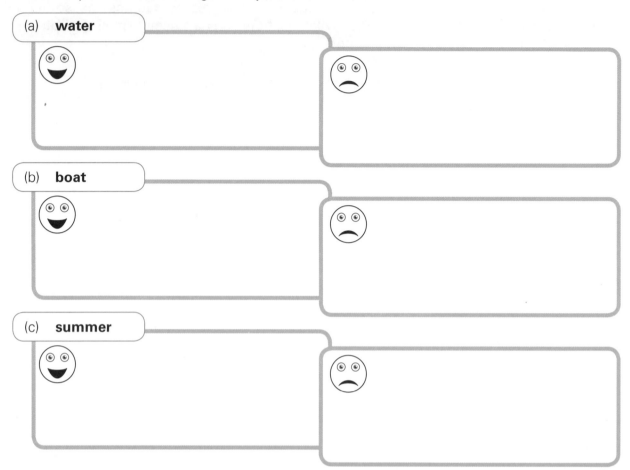

(a) **water**

(b) **boat**

(c) **summer**

Comparing adjectives

When using adjectives to compare **one** thing with another, we usually add **er**.

For example; Your boat is **long**. My boat is **longer**.

To compare more than two things, we usually add **est**.

For example; That is the **brightest** star in the sky.

Sometimes before adding **er** or **est** the last letter is doubled.

For example; It was the hottest day of the year.

Go back to page 7 if you have forgotten this spelling rule.

2. Try these.

(a) I am tall. My mother is _____. My father is the _____.

(b) Chloe is young. Her brother is _____. The baby is the _____.

(c) A bird is small. A mouse is _____. An ant is the _____.

(d) A horse is big. An elephant is _____. A whale is the _____.

(e) Mum is thin. I am _____. My sister is the _____.

Comparatives and superlatives

Comparatives compare two people or things.

I am smart**er** than my sister.

She is smart**er** than our brother.

Superlatives compare more than two people or things.

I am the smart**est** one in our family.

Go back to page 7 if you have forgotten this spelling rule.

Before adding **er** or **est** to words ending in **y**, we need to change the **y** to **i**.

For example;

happ**y**   happ**ier**   happ**iest**

3. Complete this table. Don't forget the spelling rules.

	Word	Comparative	Superlative
(a)	sad		
(b)		busier	
(c)	pretty		
(d)			heaviest
(e)	healthy		
(f)		sloppier	
(g)			funniest
(h)	silly		

4. Write the correct form of the adjective in each sentence.

(a) She is the (clever) _____ girl in our class.

(b) My mother is (fussy) _____ than yours.

(c) Our house is the (small) _____ in the street.

(d) My shoes are (new) _____ than yours.

(e) That dog is the (ugly) _____ I have ever seen.

Sometimes, instead of adding the suffixes **er** and **est** we can **use other words.** Words with two or more syllables usually use the words **more** and **most.**

For example:

fantastic   **more** fantastic   **most** fantastic

Sometimes, we can **change the word** altogether.

For example:

Jill's marks are **good.**   Mine are **better.**   Jan's are the **best.**

5. Complete this table. The words marked with an * change altogether.

	Word	Comparative	Superlative
(a)	famous		
(b)	interesting		
(c)	beautiful		
(d)	boring		
(e)	bad *		
(f)	careful		
(g)	little*		
(h)	many *		

6. Correct these sentences. Remember, the comparative compares two people or things and the superlative compares three or more.

(a) He cut the thinnest end of the rope.

_____

(b) Shane was the most fastest of all the runners.

_____

(c) The best team won the football game.

_____

(d) My horse can beat yours so it is the fastest.

_____

(e) The three of us can skate but I am the better skater.

_____

(f) The dogs were all barking but Rex was louder.

_____

Punctuation—commas

Commas are used in sentences when a pause is needed.

Read the following sentences carefully to help you understand more about commas and how they are used to:

- **Separate items in a list**

  My favourite sports are football, tennis, swimming, basketball and squash.

- **Separate clauses (a group of words with a verb and subject)**

  I rode to school, put my bag in my locker, met my friends and walked into the classroom.

- **Indicate a pause after yes or no**

  No, I haven't seen your new bike.

- **Separate the person spoken to**

  Robert, please ask your mother if she would like to come and see me.

- **Separate words giving more information**

  Skydiving, a most exciting activity, is becoming very popular.

- **Indicate a pause after direct speech**

  'Please help me find my book', Tim cried.

1. Add commas where needed in these sentences and write the reason they are needed on the line below.

   (a) Mandy enjoys eating grapes apples oranges peaches and bananas.

   _____

   (b) After he fell off his bike he decided to always wear his helmet.

   _____

   (c) Yes I do want you to help me wash the dog.

   _____

   (d) Jeremy you must be more careful.

   _____

   (e) The gardener a very hard worker has made a huge difference to our school

   environment.

   _____

   (f) 'I hate music practice' Mark complained.

   _____

Direct speech

The exact words that people say or sometimes think are referred to as **direct speech**. It is important to punctuate direct speech correctly.

The actual words spoken are enclosed within speech or quotation marks.

For example:

'Look at that beautiful new boat', Jack commented.

Note: Both single and double quotation marks are acceptable but must be used consistently.

Quotation marks are easy if you think of them as 'holding' the actual words spoken. The punctuation needed within the quotation marks is more of a challenge, but there are a few points you need to consider.

- Start every quotation with a capital letter.

- There has to be a punctuation mark before or after you close the quotation marks; a comma, a question mark, an exclamation mark or a full stop.

- Every new speaker needs a new line.

Study this dialogue.

'I wish we didn't have to wait so long', Julia moaned.

'Surely it must be our turn soon', her mother replied. 'We've certainly been here long enough.'

'Look at that!' Peter yelled.

'What are they doing?' asked Dad.

2. On the next page, rewrite the dialogue below with all the correct punctuation.

Remember:

- Before you start, underline all the direct speech so that you know what to write within the quotation marks.

- Check that you have a punctuation mark or quote mark at the end of each bit of direct speech.

- Check for capital letters at the beginning of each quote.

- Check that each new speaker starts on a new line.

I think those people are going to push in complained Mum. They wouldn't dare said Dad. Look! yelled Peter. I don't believe it, what do they think they're doing? asked Dad. What a cheek! Julia added. Are they sinking Dad? Peter asked. How wonderful Mum laughed. They got their just desserts.

True justice

_____

_____

_____

_____

_____

_____

_____

_____

_____

_____

_____

WRITING Activities

Character

1. (a) Do you think the boat owner in the narrative _True justice_ was a bully? ○ **yes** ○ **no**

   (b) Write 10 adjectives that you think could be used to describe this man.

   [ ]

   (c) Write a passage justifying your opinion of this man.

   I think the boat owner was/was not a bully because _____

   _____

   _____

   _____

   _____

Direct speech is used to report what a character says or thinks.

Look, Mum, that man is pushing in.

2. (a) On a separate sheet of paper, draw four different people who could have been standing by the ramp and write their comments in speech bubbles.

   (b) Use speech marks to rewrite their comments in the space provided.
   For example; **The young girl said, 'Look Mum, that man is pushing in'.**

1.

2.

3.

4.

There are many characters in the stories we read who could be described as bullies.

3. Read this character profile of the troll in *The three billy goats gruff*.
   Name: Troll   **Age:** Old   **Address:** Under bridge

   Appearance: ugly, hairy, loud, big and fat   **Actions:** yelling, threatening, fighting

   Personality: nasty, selfish, scary, mean, aggressive, greedy

(a) Choose a character you think is a bully from a traditional story.

(b) Write 10 adjectives to describe this person.

(c) Complete this character profile.

Name: _____

Age: _____

Address: _____

Appearance: _____

_____

_____

Personality: _____

_____

_____

Actions: _____

_____

_____

4. Imagine that this character's personality changes and he/she is no longer a bully.

(a) Write 10 adjectives to describe this changed character.

(b) How would this affect the story?

_____

_____

_____

Choose a topic from the box below and write a narrative. Use the plan to guide your ideas. When you are ready, write the story in full on a separate sheet of paper. Try to make your characters believable. Start new paragraphs for new ideas. Use interesting verbs instead of 'said'.

The school bully	**The bad sport**	**Wait your turn**
A boating mishap	**In trouble again**	**The gang**

Title	
Orientation	
Characters (appearance, personality, likely actions)	
Setting/Location	
Time	
Initiating event	
What event starts the action?	
How does this involve the characters?	
Complication	
What problem do the characters have?	
What caused the problem?	
Resolution	
How is the problem solved?	
Conclusion	
What happened in the end?	

When you have completed your story, proofread and edit it using the following questions as a guide.

Checklist

Title of the narrative: _____

1. **Title**

    (a)   Does the title indicate what the story is about?..........................○ **yes** ○ **no**

    (b)   Does it get the attention of the reader? ....○ **yes** ○ **no**

2. **Orientation**

    (a)   Does the beginning draw the reader into the characters' world?....○ **yes** ○ **no**

    (b)   Are the characters believable? ....○ **yes** ○ **no**

    (c)   Do their actions fit their personalities?...○ **yes** ○ **no**

    (d)   Is the setting realistic? ....○ **yes** ○ **no**

3. **Initiating event**

    Is the problem known at the beginning of the story?............................○ **yes** ○ **no**

4. **Complication**

    Is the problem believable?...○ **yes** ○ **no**

5. **Resolution**

    (a)   Does the resolution fit the complication?..○ **yes** ○ **no**

    (b)   Have the problems been solved? ....○ **yes** ○ **no**

6. **Conclusion**

    Is the ending satisfying to the reader? ....○ **yes** ○ **no**

7. **Punctuation and spelling**

    Have you checked the following?

    (a)   Spelling – use a dictionary or ask someone ....○ **yes** ○ **no**

    (b)   Punctuation – including capital letters, full stops,

    question marks, commas and direct speech. ....○ **yes** ○ **no**

    (c)   Paragraphs for new ideas..○ **yes** ○ **no**

8. **Vocabulary**

    (a)   Have you used some interesting adjectives? ....○ **yes** ○ **no**

    (b)   Have you used any compound words? ....○ **yes** ○ **no**

    (c)   Have you used interesting verbs instead of **said**? ....○ **yes** ○ **no**

1. Choose a title from the box then plan, and write, a narrative on a separate sheet of paper.

    > **A fishy tale**   **The grumpy old man**
    >
    > **The boat ride**   **Gone boating**
    >
    > **It's not fair**   **One good turn deserves another**

2. A narrative has five parts.

    (a) The _____ indicates what the story is about.

    (b) The _____ tells who, what, where and when.

    (c) The _____ tells the problem facing the main character(s).

    (d) The _____ tells how the problem is solved.

    (e) The _____ tells what happens in the end.

3. Join the antonyms.

    (a) like   •   •   hinder

    (b) fair   •   •   clever

    (c) broad   •   •   dislike

    (d) energetic •   •   narrow

    (e) stupid   •   •   float

    (f) help   •   •   unfair

    (g) sink   •   •   lazy

4. Add **un**, **dis** or **in** to make antonyms.

    (a) cut _____

    (b) interested _____

    _____

    (c) correct _____

    (d) like _____

    (e) ability _____

    _____

    (f) kind _____

5. Write these words in the correct columns.

    > **tunnel**   **boat**   **happily**   **fishing**   **deserved**
    >
    > **bait**   **sand**   **stupidly**   **people**

one syllable	two syllables	three syllables

6. Add another syllable to these words to make a new word.

    (a) look _____

    (b) teach _____

    (c) sad _____

    (d) child _____

    (e) unkind _____

    (f) like _____

7. Complete this table. Don't forget the spelling rules.

	Word	Comparative	Superlative
(a)		happier	
(b)	wealthy		
(c)			saddest
(d)			busiest
(e)		more interesting	
(f)	good		best
(g)	hard		
(h)	comfortable		

8. Add commas where needed.

(a) My mother a very wise lady always wears a hat in the sun.

(b) Take your fishing line hooks sinkers bait and tackle box with you.

(c) The men climbed into their boat started the motor set off at speed and went nowhere fast.

(d) 'Dad can we take the boat out again next weekend?'

(e) 'Please grab the rope and pull us in' said Dad.

(f) Waterskiing a sport enjoyed by people of all ages is a popular family activity.

9. Add quotation marks where needed.

Must you always be so impatient? Dad remarked.

His son replied, I'm not always in a hurry Dad, but I'm really late today .

You should get up earlier , advised his father.

But it's so cold, his son replied, I just can't get out of bed .

Well, it should be warmer soon , his dad replied.

Thermometers

> Reports give **facts clearly** without **unnecessary information** or **opinions**.

Read this report about thermometers.

Thermometers

A thermometer is an instrument used to measure temperature.

Early thermometers

In 1592, Galileo, an Italian scientist, made the first working thermometer or thermoscope. It was a long-necked glass tube full of air which was placed upside down in a bowl of alcohol. When the tube was heated, the level of alcohol inside the tube sank because the warm air trapped in it expanded and took up more space. The level rose when the tube was cooler and the air inside contracted, taking up less space.

The medical thermometer

Professor Sanctorius, an Italian doctor, invented the medical thermometer in 1612 and used it on his first patient, who had a fever. Another idea of his was to add a scale by marking the glass tube with 110 marks from cold (melting snow) to hot (candle heat).

Mercury was found to work better than the water or the alcohol that had been used inside the glass tubes.

How a medical thermometer works

Mercury inside the bulb at the bottom of the thermometer expands when it warms up and is forced out of the bulb end up inside the narrow tube. There is a small notch near the bottom of the tube which prevents the mercury falling back into the bulb. This allows the doctor or nurse to read the patient's temperature from the scale marked on the side of the thermometer.

Scales

Early scientists devised their own scales and there were over 35 different scales being used by 1700. Scientists couldn't compare information and so finally just two scales were selected. They were:

The Fahrenheit scale

This scale was developed by Daniel Fahrenheit in 1714. The freezing point of water is 32 °F and water boils at 212 °F. The Fahrenheit scale is still used today in many countries, including the USA.

The Celsius scale

In 1742, Anders Celsius, a Swedish astronomer, invented this scale. It uses 0 °C for the melting point of ice and 100 °C for the boiling point of water.

Many countries use this scale today. Some, like Australia, changed from the Fahrenheit to the Celsius scale in the 20th century.

Conclusion

Thermometers are an integral part of modern society and it would be difficult to imagine life without them.

Partner activity

1. Tell your partner about an occasion when you had a high temperature. Make sure that you provide information about:

when it happened	**where you were**
whether a thermometer was used	**what caused it**
who helped you	**how you were treated**
what happened	**what the results were**

Remember: Reports give facts clearly and without unnecessary information or opinions. Try to provide your information in a factual way. Instead of describing how you and others felt at the time, clearly state the facts about the incident.

2. Listen carefully to your partner's report and answer the questions.

   (a) What is your partner's name? _____

   (b) How did your partner know he/she had a temperature? _____
   _____

   (c) Where did it happen? _____

   (d) When did it happen? _____

   (e) What caused the problem? _____
   _____

   (f) Who provided assistance? _____

   (g) What treatment was given? _____
   _____

   (h) What happened and how did it end? _____
   _____
   _____

   (i) Did your partner give a clear concise report? ◯ **yes** ◯ **no**

(j) What is one thing your partner did well?	(k) What is one way the report could have been improved?

Structure

This report has:

    A title: Identifies the subject.

    Classification: *What is it?* Provides information about the focus of the report.

    Description: *When* it was invented.

        Where it was invented.

        Who was responsible.

        What it does.

        How it works.

        Special features.

    Conclusion: A summary or comment.

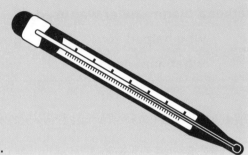

Read the report *Thermometers* again and answer the questions.

1. **Title**   What is the title of the report? _____

        Write an appropriate alternative title. _____

2. **Classification** What is a thermometer? _____

        _____

3. **Description**   (a) When did Galileo make the first thermometer? _____

        (b) What happened to the level of alcohol in the tube when it was hot?

            _____

        (c) Why did the level change? _____

            _____

        (d) Who developed the first medical thermometer?

            _____

        (e) Why doesn't the mercury go back down into the bulb of a medical thermometer when it cools down?

            _____

            _____

        (f) What two scales are still used to measure temperature?

            _____

4. **Conclusion**   Are thermometers important today? ◯ yes ◯ no

Reading for information

1. True or false? Colour the correct answers.

   (a) When the air inside Galileo's 'thermometer' was heated, the level of alcohol in the tube rose. ◯ **true** ◯ **false**

   (b) Sanctorius was a doctor. ◯ **true** ◯ **false**

   (c) Mercury is used in most thermometers. ◯ **true** ◯ **false**

   (d) Australia changed from Celsius to the Fahrenheit scale. ◯ **true** ◯ **false**

   (e) Water boils at 100 °F. ◯ **true** ◯ **false**

Reading for understanding

1. Explain why there were so many different scales developed around the world to measure temperature.

   _____

   _____

   _____

2. Explain why the temperature on a hot day in Australia in 1950 was about 100 degrees and now a hot day is about 38 degrees.

   _____

   _____

   _____

3. People who are sick often have a high temperature. How did doctors know that someone had a fever before the thermometer was invented?

   _____

   _____

   _____

4. Explain why there is a small notch near the bottom of the tube of a medical thermometer.

   _____

   _____

   _____

Applying your knowledge

1. (a) Make a temperature chart showing changes in a patient's temperature over 24 hours using the information below.

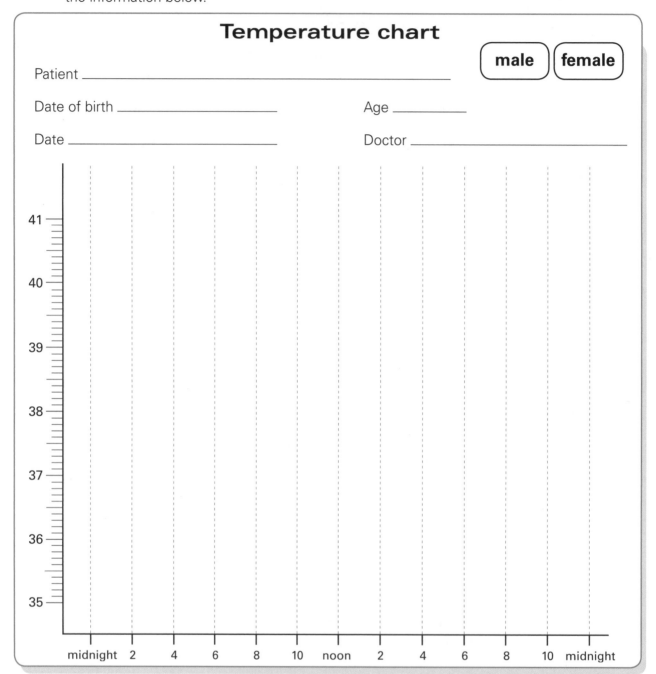

Temperature chart

male   female

Patient _____

Date of birth _____   Age _____

Date _____   Doctor _____

Midnight	2 am	4 am	6 am	8 am	10.00 am	Noon
37.4	**38.0**	**39.0**	**40.7**	**39.0**	**38.6**	**37.8**
2 pm	4 pm	6 pm	8 pm	10 pm	Midnight	
36.9	**37.0**	**38.1**	**38.8**	**37.1**	**40.2**	

(b) At what time was the patient's temperature the highest? _____

(c) When was the temperature the lowest? _____

(d) Was the patient's temperature higher during daylight or darkness? _____

Making new words

1. Add **c** and rearrange the letters to make a new word.

   (a) Add **c** to sole and get a word meaning nearby. _____

   (b) Add **c** to real to get a word meaning easy to see. _____

   (c) Add **c** to pale to get a word meaning somewhere to go. _____

   (d) Add **c** to harm to get a word meaning to walk. _____

   (e) Add **c** to moment to get a word meaning something you say. _____

Double letters

2. Complete each word with a double letter.

   (a) le_____ _____uce

   (b) ca_____ _____age

   (c) sho_____ _____ing

   (d) mi_____ _____ion

   (e) pa_____ _____ot

   (f) gi_____ _____le

   (g) di_____ _____erent

   (h) wi _____ _____er

Word chains

3. (a) Change **toad** to **hole** in three moves by changing one letter at a time to form a new word.

t	o	a	d
h	o	l	e

(b) Change **seal** to **felt** in three moves.

s	e	a	l
f	e	l	t

(c) Change **chess** to **cheap** in three moves.

c	h	e	s	s
c	h	e	a	p

Find the letter

4. Find the missing letter that will make two words. The first letter has been added to make the words tramp and pasta. The missing letters in the shaded boxes will form a word.

(a)

t	r	a	m	p	a	s	t	a
g	l	i	d		x	i	l	e
t	r	e	a		a	b	l	e
f	l	u	t		n	t	e	r
f	l	o	u		i	v	e	r

The boy's name is:

(b)

m	a	g	i	c	r	a	f	t
p	i	z	z		w	a	k	e
s	t	e	a		o	u	s	e
s	n	a	k		v	e	r	y
f	i	n	a		i	o	n	s

The animal is:

5. Cross out the letters **b f g k** and write the hidden messages.

(a) **abftkherbmofmbgektefrgisfbafngifngstkbkrubfmentfb**

(b) **tfghfekrfmgombfektegrsbmgebaksurekbtbefmfpebraktburge**

(c) **dgobfcfgtgokrsgkbusgbeftgfhkbefrgbmofgbmebfftergksg**

6.   Complete the crossword. The words are from the report *Thermometers*.

Across

2   Make bigger
4.   Series of degrees
8.   Indentation
10.   Become smaller
12.   Long hollow cylinder
13.   Put
15.   Temperature scale
18.   Degree of heat
20   High temperature
22.   Dilated part of a glass tube
23.   Choose
24.   Caused by illness

Down

1.   Opposite of hot
3.   Cares for patients
5.   Region of a nation
6.   A liquid metal
7.   Tool
9.   Not the top or bottom
11.   Something you can see through
14   Studies science
16   Determine size
17.   Person under medical treatment
19.   Bubbles up
21.   Liquid compound of oxygen and hydrogen

Plurals

The plural of most English words is usually made simply by adding **s**.

For example: thermometer**s**   dentist**s**

Revise the following rules remembering that there are often exceptions to every rule.

Rule

Nouns ending is **x, s, z, ch** or **sh** add **es** to make the plural easier to say.

For example: punch – punch**es**

Note: If **ch** makes a **k** sound, just add **s**.

For example: stoma**chs**

Rule

Nouns ending in **f** or **fe** change the **f** or **fe** to **v**, then add **es**.

For example: kni**fe** – kni**ves**   whar**f** – whar**ves**

Note: There are some exceptions.

For example: beliefs, chefs, reefs, chiefs

Some words can be spelled two different ways.

For example: hoofs, hooves

Remember: Always consult a dictionary if you are unsure.

1.   Write the plurals of the words in brackets.

(a)   The spaceship landed near the _____ (tree).

(b)   The _____ (bus) took the _____ (class) to the zoo.

(c)   Seatbelts have saved many _____ (life).

(d)   All the _____ (lunch) were packed into

      _____ (box) by the _____ (parent).

(e)   The _____ (elf) played _____ (trick)

      on the _____ (witch) by hiding their

      _____ (broomstick) in the _____ (bush).

(f)   The queen's daughters are _____ (princess) and her sons are

      _____ (prince).

(g)   The beating of their horses' _____ (hoof) warned their

      _____ (enemy) that the _____ (soldier) were advancing.

(h)   The girls left their _____ (shampoo), _____

      (brush) and _____ (comb) in the change rooms after their swimming

      carnival, but they remembered their swimsuits, _____ (swimming cap)

      and _____ (towel).

Rule

Words ending in **y** after a consonant change the **y** to **i** before adding **es**.
    For example: stor**y** – stor**ies**   bab**y** – bab**ies**

2. Write the plural of these words.

(a) family

(b) fairy

(c) monkey

(d) library

(e) mystery

(f) fly

(g) turkey

(h) tray

3. Write the plurals of the words in brackets.

(a) There are many different _____ of books in the library. (category)

(b) The truck collected milk from twenty _____ before returning to the factory. (dairy)

(c) My father's plane didn't land until after midnight because of _____ at two airports in America. (delay)

(d) The harbour _____ were cancelled because of the very high winds and rough seas. (ferry)

(e) They completed a number of _____ before deciding where the pond would be built. (survey)

Rule

Some words ending in **o**, including modern words, just add **s**, but others add **es**.

    For example: videos   yoyos
                   tomatoes   volcanoes

There are also some words that have both **s** and **es** accepted.

    For example: mangoes   mangos
                   mosquitoes   mosquitos
                   zeroes   zeros

Note: • If in doubt, consult a dictionary.

       • Plurals of words associated with music often just add **s**.

    For example: pianos   banjos   duos   trios   cellos
                   sopranos   solos   radios   altos

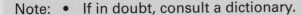

---

4. Write the plurals of these words in the correct columns. You may need to use your dictionary.

| piano | mosquito | dingo | potato | radio | studio | kilo |
| hero | echo | cargo | buffalo | motto | torpedo | hippo | tornado |

s	es	either

Irregular plurals

The plurals of some words change.   For example: man   men

5. Write the plurals of these words.

(a) foot _____   (b) child _____

(c) mouse _____   (d) ox _____

(e) woman _____   (f) goose _____

(g) tooth _____   (h) die _____

Words with no singular

Some things that come in pairs are often already plurals.

For example: tweezers

6. Complete these sentences.

(a) Mum needed her g_____ to read the recipe.

(b) The birdwatchers used b_____ to see the birds high up in the trees.

(c) The children wore p_____ to bed.

(d) Dad was given a new belt to put on his t_____.

(e) He picked the meat up from the barbecue using some t_____.

(f) The hairdresser dropped her very expensive s_____ on the floor and damaged them.

(g) Amphibians are an interesting s_____ of animal.

(h) The police entered the p_____ because the security alarm was activated.

Words with the same forms

Some words have the same form for both singular and plural, especially some types of birds, fish or animals.

For example: deer   fish   sheep

7. Write a sentence using each of these words.

(a) trout _____

_____

(b) reindeer _____

_____

(c) bison _____

_____

(d) dozen _____

_____

(e) innings _____

_____

(f) carp _____

_____

LANGUAGE FEATURES

Prepositions

Prepositions connect one thing with another, showing how they are related.

For example; Georgie spent hours **on** the phone talking **to** her friends **after** school.

1. Complete each sentence using a preposition from the box.

(a) Please refrain _____ talking during the film.

(b) Netball is a similar game _____ basketball.

(c) I am depending _____ you to help in the garden.

(d) Those children have interfered _____ my computer.

(e) Do you think that house is worthy _____ another look?

(f) She is so understanding that all her friends confide _____ her.

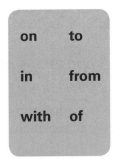

on	to
in	from
with	of

Prepositions of time

Some prepositions refer to time; for example, I clean my teeth *before* I go to bed.

2. Underline the prepositions of time.

(a) Look before you leap.

(b) Would you like a coffee after work?

(c) During the holidays I had the flu.

(d) He has played football since he was in primary school.

(e) I'm going to practise this until I get it right.

3. Write a sentence using each preposition of time.

(a) while

_____

_____

(b) during

_____

_____

(c) at

_____

_____

(d) after

_____

_____

(e) since

_____

_____

Prepositions of place

4. Where is it?

Write sentences on the next page using prepositions to tell where these things are.

(a) patient   (b) clock

(c) slippers   (d) nurse

(e) pillows   (f) thermometer

(a)

(b)

(c)

(d)

(e)

(f)

5. Use a preposition of place to complete each sentence.

(a) The water leaked in _____ the door.

(b) The children ran _____ the playground.

(c) My tooth was put _____ a jar and handed to me.

(d) Before reaching the wharf, the ship had to sail _____ the bridge.

(e) We wandered _____ the shops looking for some new shoes.

Opposites

6. Change the bold preposition to the opposite using the words in the box. Write the new sentences in the spaces provided.

below	*inside*	*off*	*after*	*with*	*around*	*down*	*under*

(a) **Before** breakfast, John climbed **up** the stairs.

_____

(b) The boys rowed the boat **across** the lake.

_____

(c) Our plane flew **above** the clouds to avoid the storm.

_____

(d) The children jumped **on** the trampoline **outside** the building.

_____

(e) The passenger train travelled **over** the bridge.

_____

(f) I can swim fast **without** my swim fins.

_____

> *Idioms*
>
> Idioms are sayings used in everyday speech.
> For example: To be caught red-handed
>   To know the ropes.

7. Complete these idioms using the correct preposition from the box.

from	*against*	*with*	*around*	*to*	*up*	*in*	*for*

(a) To beat _____ the bush.

(b) To give _____ the ghost.

(c) To start _____ scratch.

(d) To nip it _____ the bud.

(e) To go _____ the grain.

(f) Welcome _____ open arms.

(g) An exception _____ the rule.

(h) To go _____ broke.

8. Underline the preposition in each sentence.

(a) The angry elephant charged through the village.

(b) I did well in all my exams except maths.

(c) The train travelled towards the mountains.

(d) He left his muddy boots outside the door.

(e) The artist is proud of his work.

(f) The children walked to school.

(g) During the holidays I'm going horse riding.

(h) He was disgusted by the football fans' behaviour.

Descriptions

When writing the description part of a report, the information or facts provided change according to the focus of the report as stated in the classification.

> For example:
>
> When writing about a tool, the focus may be on the uses of the tool rather than its appearance. You might include some of the following facts.
>
> Classification: Name of tool
>
> Description: Why is it used?
>
>   When is it used?
>
>   How is it used?

1. Write a description suitable for a report about a tool you use; for example, a pencil or a toothbrush. Remember to write **facts** not **opinions** and to focus on **why**, **when** and **how** you use this tool. Use clear and concise language.

Classification: _____

Description: _____

_____

_____

_____

_____

_____

_____

_____

_____

_____

_____

_____

_____

_____

2. (a) Write a description of a different tool using clear, concise language. Remember to focus on **why**, **when** and **how** it is used, but don't say what it is.

Classification: _Mystery tool_

Description: _____

_____

_____

_____

_____

_____

_____

_____

_____

_____

_____

_____

_____

_____

_____

_____

_____

_____

_____

_____

_____

_____

(b) Ask a partner to work out what your mystery tool is and to draw it on a separate sheet of paper.

(c) Was your partner correct? ⵔ **yes** ⵔ **no**

Choose a topic for a report from the box below and use the plan to prepare it before writing it in full on a separate sheet of paper. Remember to use facts, not opinions. You may need to research to find some important facts.

telephones	watches	biros	stethoscopes
radios	microwave ovens	telescopes	cameras

Title:

Classification (Type): _____

_____

Description:

What do they look like?

What are they used for?

Who invented them?

Where and when were they invented?

Any other important facts?

Conclusion: _____

_____

After you have written your report in full, use the checklist below to edit and proofread your work.

You will be self-editing for:

Spelling   Punctuation

Grammar   Sentence structure

You will be using a peer editor to check:

Sense   Use of facts

Checklist

Title of report: _____

1. Does your report include:

   (a) what they look like?.. ○ **yes** ○ **no**

   (b) what they're used for? .... ○ **yes** ○ **no**

   (c) who invented them? .... ○ **yes** ○ **no**

   (d) where and when they were invented? .... ○ **yes** ○ **no**

   (e) any other important facts? .... ○ **yes** ○ **no**

2. Have you written facts, not opinions? .... ○ **yes** ○ **no**

3. Do you have a concluding statement?....................... ○ **yes** ○ **no**

4. Have you corrected any spelling errors?.................. ○ **yes** ○ **no**

5. Have you used capital letters and full stops correctly? .... ○ **yes** ○ **no**

6. Did your peer editor:

   (a) understand your report? .... ○ **yes** ○ **no**

   (b) believe your facts are true? .... ○ **yes** ○ **no**

1. Choose a topic from the box below and write a report. Use a report plan to help you to organise your ideas before writing your report in full on a separate sheet of paper.

bicycles	mobile phones	combs
tin-openers	kettles	scissors

2. Reports should provide facts not _____ and should not have unnecessary

_____.

3. Write the plurals of these words.

   (a) church _____
   (b) family _____

   (c) tomato _____
   (d) video _____

   (e) piano _____
   (f) tooth _____

   (g) deer _____
   (h) jeans _____

   (i) bus _____
   (j) fox _____

4. Change the bold words from singular (one) to plural (more than one) and rewrite the sentences.

   (a) My grandfather told me **a story** about his past which I really enjoyed.

   _____

   _____

   (b) The **wife** of King Henry VIII of England **was** in danger of losing **her life**.

   _____

   _____

   (c) I often visit the **library** in Vienna looking for books about **adventure** and **mystery**.

   _____

   _____

5. Underline the prepositions and write **time** or **place** in the space provided.

   (a) During the weekend I played football.

   (b) I finished my homework before dinner.

   (c) Put your bag in your room.

   (d) I left my bike outside last night.

   (e) Why don't you ride your bicycle to school?

6. Write a sentence using each of these words as a preposition.

(a) below

(b) into

(c) around

(d) behind

(e) until

7. Rewrite the sentences using the opposite preposition.

(a) He ran **up** the stairs.

_____

(b) Beth poured the milk **from** the jug.

_____

(c) The tree's roots were growing **above** the ground.

_____

(d) The soldiers marched **under** the bridge.

_____

(e) We turned the heater **on**.

_____

8. Complete these idioms using the correct prepositions from the box.

on	below	by	in	over	out

(a) Head _____ heels

(b) Saved _____ the bell

(c) Hit _____ the belt

(d) Fish _____ of water

(e) To hit the nail _____ the head

(f) To be _____ hot water